GREEN

FOUNTAINHEAD PRESS V SERIES

Doctor Who
"Forest of the Dead"
"The Doctor, The Widow and The Wardrobe"
Wall-E
Pocahontas
Erin Brockovitch

Edited by
Brooke Rollins and Lee Bauknight

Our green initiatives include:

Electronic Products
We deliver products in non-paper form whenever possible. This includes pdf downloadables, flash drives, & CDs.

Electronic Samples
We use Xample, a new electronic sampling system. Instructor samples are sent via a personalized web page that links to pdf downloads.

FSC Certified Printers
All of our printers are certified by the Forest Service Council which promotes environmentally and socially responsible management of the world's forests. This program allows consumer groups, individual consumers, and businesses to work together hand-in-hand to promote responsible use of the world's forests as a renewable and sustainable resource.

Recycled Paper
Most of our products are printed on a minimum of 30% post-consumer waste recycled paper.

Support of Green Causes
When we do print, we donate a portion of our revenue to green causes. Listed below are a few of the organizations that have received donations from Fountainhead Press. We welcome your feedback and suggestions for contributions, as we are always searching for worthy initiatives.

Rainforest 2 Reef
Environmental Working Group

Design by Susan Moore

Books may be purchased for educational purposes.

For information, please call or write:

1-800-586-0330

Fountainhead Press
Southlake, TX 76092

Web Site: www.fountainheadpress.com
E-mail: customerservice@fountainheadpress.com

First Edition

ISBN: 978-1-59871-415-9

Printed in the United States of America

INTRODUCTION TO THE FOUNTAINHEAD PRESS V SERIES

By Brooke Rollins and Lee Bauknight
Series Editors

The *Fountainhead Press V Series* is a new collection of single-topic readers that takes a unique look at some of today's most pressing issues. Designed to give writing students a more nuanced introduction to public discourse—on the environment, on food, and on digital life, to name a few of the topics—the books feature writing, research, and invention prompts that can be adapted to nearly any kind of college writing class. Each *V Series* textbook focuses on a single issue and includes multi-genre and multimodal readings and assignments that move the discourse beyond the most familiar patterns of debate—patterns usually fettered by entrenched positions and often obsessed with "winning."

The ultimate goal of the series is to help writing students—who tend to hover on the periphery of public discourse—think, explore, find their voices, and skillfully compose texts in a variety of media and genres. Not only do the books help students think about compelling issues and how they might address them, they also give students the practice they need to develop their research, rhetorical, and writing skills. Together, the readings, prompts, and longer assignments show students how to add their voices to the conversations about these issues in meaningful and productive ways.

With enough readings and composing tasks to sustain an entire quarter or semester, and inexpensive enough to be used in combination with other rhetorics and readers, the *Fountainhead Press V Series* provides instructors with the flexibility to build the writing courses they want and need to teach. An instructor interested in deeply exploring environmental issues, for example, could design a semester- or quarter-long course using *Green*, the first of the *V Series* texts. On the other hand, an instructor who wanted to teach discrete units on different issues could use two or more of the *V Series* books. In either case, the texts would give students ample opportunity—and a variety of ways—to engage with the issues at hand.

The *V Series* uses the term "composition" in its broadest sense. Of course, the textbooks provide students plenty of opportunities to write, but they also include assignments that take students beyond the page. Books in the series encourage students to explore other modes of communication by prompting them to design web sites, for example; to produce videos, posters, and presentations; to conduct primary and secondary research; and to develop projects with community partners that might incorporate any number of these skills. Ultimately, we have designed the *Fountainhead Press V Series* to work for teachers and students. With their carefully chosen readings, built-in flexibility, and sound rhetorical grounding, the *V Series* books would be a dynamic and user-friendly addition to any writing class.

Table of Contents

INTRODUCTION
SHADES OF GREEN

By Brooke Rollins and Lee Bauknight

In the months following the April 20, 2010, explosion of the Deepwater Horizon rig off the coast of Louisiana, an estimated 200 million gallons of crude oil gushed into the Gulf of Mexico, ravaging delicate wetland and ocean ecosystems and the birds, sea turtles, dolphins, whales, shrimp, and fish (to name only a few threatened species) that inhabit them.

No one yet knows the long term affects of this disaster. Although the well was capped and the oil flow staunched in mid-July, and relief wells that would provide a permanent solution to the leak were near completion, coastal regions will be forced to deal with the effects of the disaster for decades, perhaps even lifetimes. "Every oil spill is different," *The New York Times* reported on July 18, "but the thread that unites [them] … is a growing scientific awareness of the persistent damage that spills can do—and of just how long oil can linger in the environment,

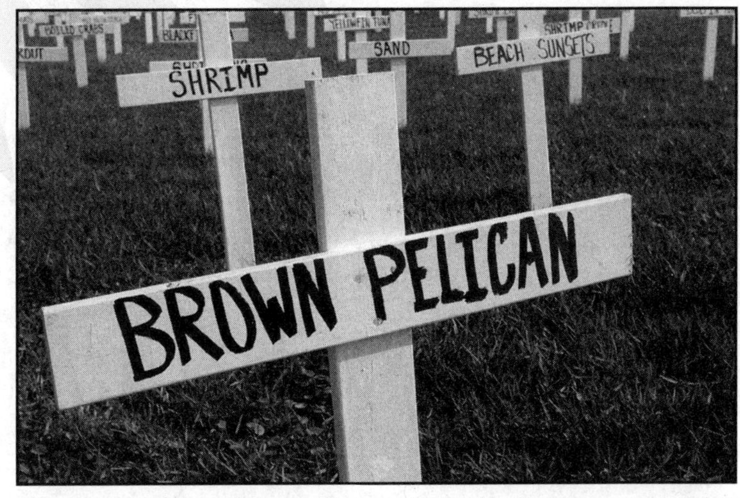

A mock cemetery built by residents of Grand Isle, Louisiana, in June 2010 mourns the losses caused by the BP oil spill. "Everything is dying," one Louisianan said at a town hall meeting in Plaquemines Parish, and that feeling was common as BP, the federal government, and others tried to stop the massive flow of oil into the Gulf. That finally happened in late July, but the extent of the damage to the area remains unknown. (Photo by Getty Images.) Used with permission.

hidden in out-of-the-way spots." How many years might it take for populations of birds and fish to recover to normal levels? Which species might be pushed past the brink? How long before the spawning grounds of shrimp and crabs recover? When will the fisheries, closed because their waters were contaminated with poisonous sludge, re-open and sustain the livelihoods of the coastal communities that built them?

Another frightening possibility is that the disaster may have opened the Gulf coast to future destruction: As the marshlands now soaked with oil slowly die, the physical barrier that slows the force of fierce hurricanes erodes, and the coastline becomes even more susceptible to damage from storms.

Clearly, there is no upside to devastation this profound, but if the BP oil disaster has shown us anything, it is that our seemingly boundless reliance on fossil fuels—and our drive to extract them from the planet's depths—is one of the most dangerous threats to the natural world. The Gulf disaster is just one powerful example of this disturbing truth, especially in the United States, where many of us enjoy lifestyles of relative comfort and convenience, often at the cost of our natural surroundings. According to *National Geographic*'s third annual "Greendex," a comprehensive study of the per capita environmental impact of 17 countries, Americans have the largest so-called "carbon footprints." From our love of plastic water bottles to SUVs and plasma screen TVs, our patterns of energy consumption are the least sustainable in the world.

Although experts may debate the best way to address the threats to our environment, most agree that the situation is dire and that we cannot maintain our present course. Against this backdrop, *Green* provides a path through the myriad perspectives on environmental issues. Rooted in philosophy, science, politics, history, pop culture, and personal experience, the texts collected in the pages that follow consider the environmental crises we face and argue about how and why we should try to do something to protect the planet—and ourselves. *Green* is by no means comprehensive—no single volume could hope to be—but we have put together a selection of interesting, creative, and sometimes unconventional readings and images that we believe will help you engage with environmental issues in informed and strategic ways.

We have included lyrics and poetry, memoirs and other personal writing; an excerpt from a graphic novel and other visual texts; researched arguments, guides, magazine and newspaper pieces, and book chapters. Each of these selections stands on its own as a significant contribution to the public discourse about the environment, and taken together they create a narrative—a complicated story about America's relationship to, appropriation of, and identification with nature. You may be familiar with some of the plotlines of this story, but the ending remains unclear.

In addition to written and visual texts, *Green* includes research, invention, and composing prompts that will help you add your voice to the ongoing conversations about the environment. As you read the selections and work through the corresponding prompts, we hope you will keep an eye trained beyond the page. Indeed, many of the prompts will allow you to link up, not only with your classmates, but also with multi-genre texts and ongoing environmental projects. And you'll be doing more than writing here: Prompts and other assignments in the book will encourage you to explore various modes of communication—by asking you to design a website, for example; to produce videos, posters, and presentations; to conduct primary and secondary research; and to develop projects with community partners that might incorporate any number of these skills.

One of the things we hope you'll begin to see as you move through the book is how profoundly connected American identity and identities are to the environment. The problem, of course, is that for much of our history, these identities have been rooted in a sense of appropriation. The Europeans who first settled along the Atlantic Coast recognized the beauty and bounty of the land, and this recognition grew as settlers moved south and west and the United States grew into the nation that it is today. But along with this appreciation for the natural wonder that is our country, we have also felt, for centuries, a sense of ownership—this land is ours, and we can do with it as we please. And despite strains of environmentalism that are nearly as old as the United States itself, what we have done to the land (and the water, the sky, and all of the creatures that inhabit them) often has not been good. All of which is to say that, just as we affect and define the natural world, as the readings in *Green* show, so too does nature affect and define us. We can again look to the Gulf Coast to see this dynamic in action: In any environmental disaster, we—our livelihoods, our cultures, and our psyches—are just as much a part of the damaged environment as the fouled water, air, land, and animals.

To close our introduction, and to open the readings, we turn now to another measure of our connection to the environment and its connection to us, popular music. What follows are the lyrics from two songs—"This Land Is Your Land" by Woody Guthrie, from the 1940s, and "Mercy Mercy Me (The Ecology)" by Marvin Gaye, from the 1970s. Each of these, though separated by decades, speaks to our relationship to and treatment of the land, the natural world, and the planet. And, like much of the rest of *Green*, they also reveal identities that are built on connections to and concerns for the environment.

When folk music icon Woody Guthrie first sang in the 1940s that "this land was made for you and me," he was proclaiming his belief that America—the land and all that it represented—was meant for everyone, not a privileged few. While "This Land Is Your Land" is more political than environmental, a close reading shows the intricate links between America the place, the American spirit, and Americans' sense of identity. Coming nearly thirty years later, during a flowering of environmental awareness and advocacy, soul legend Marvin Gaye's "Mercy Mercy Me (The Ecology)" gets straight to the point about ongoing threats to the environment: "Oh, things ain't what they used to be / No, no / Where did all the blue sky go?"

To take the comparison a step further, do an online search for the lyrics to "Wake Up America," the 2010 song co-written by Miley Cyrus. In it, the pop princess expresses the mix of concern and confusion that many of us feel about the environment today: We know something needs to be done, but we're not sure what.

THIS LAND IS YOUR LAND
By Woody Guthrie

This land is your land This land is my land
From California to the New York island;
From the red wood forest to the Gulf Stream waters
This land was made for you and Me.

As I was walking that ribbon of highway,
I saw above me that endless skyway:
I saw below me that golden valley:
This land was made for you and me.

I've roamed and rambled and I followed my footsteps
To the sparkling sands of her diamond deserts;
And all around me a voice was sounding:
This land was made for you and me.

When the sun came shining, and I was strolling,
And the wheat fields waving and the dust clouds rolling,
As the fog was lifting a voice was chanting:
This land was made for you and me.

As I went walking I saw a sign there
And on the sign it said "No Trespassing."
But on the other side it didn't say nothing,

That side was made for you and me.
In the shadow of the steeple I saw my people,
By the relief office I seen my people;
As they stood there hungry, I stood there asking

Is this land made for you and me?
Nobody living can ever stop me,
As I go walking that freedom highway;
Nobody living can ever make me turn back
This land was made for you and me.

MERCY MERCY ME (THE ECOLOGY)
By Marvin Gaye

Oh, mercy mercy me
Oh, things ain't what they used to be
No, no

Where did all the blue sky go?
Poison is the wind that blows
From the north, east, south, and sea
Oh, mercy mercy me
Oh, things ain't what they used to be
No, no

Oil wasted on the oceans and upon our seas
Fish full of mercury
Oh, mercy mercy me
Oh, things ain't what they used to be
No, no

Radiation in the ground and in the sky
Animals and birds who live nearby are dying
Oh, mercy mercy me
Oh, things ain't what they used to be

What about this overcrowded land?
How much more abuse from man can you stand?
My sweet Lord
My sweet Lord
My sweet Lord

Explore

Pop culture—as expressed through music, movies, TV, books, websites, and other media—can be an excellent indicator of the values and concerns of the society that produces it. Using the Guthrie, Gaye, and Cyrus song lyrics as models, find at least two other pop culture texts that express a point of view or make an argument about the environment. How do these texts convey their messages? How do they connect with their audiences? Do you think pop culture texts are an effective means of arguing for change? Why or why not?

Collaborate

With a group of classmates, use Google, Bing, or another search engine to find performances (audio or video) of "This Land Is Your Land," "Mercy Mercy Me (the Ecology)," and "Wake Up America." After studying the lyrics and listening to or watching the performances, come to a consensus on the following questions: What are the most significant rhetorical differences between lyrics written on a page and songs performed by an artist? Do you think one format is more effective than the other as an argument? Why?

Compare Cyrus's cheery tone to
Ethridge's imploring & subdued tone
significance of wake up America
&
I need to wake up

One of the world's greatest and most influential living scientists, biologist Edward O. Wilson has written numerous books and won two Pulitzer Prizes. "For the Love of Life" is the penultimate chapter of his 2002 book The Future of Life, *which one reviewer called "a meditation on the splendor of our biosphere and the dangers we pose to it."*

FOR THE LOVE OF LIFE

By Edward O. Wilson

Have you ever wondered how we will be remembered a thousand years from now, when we are as remote as Charlemagne? Many would be satisfied with a list that includes the following: *the technoscientific revolution continued, globalized, and unstoppable; computer capacity approaching that of the human brain; robotic auxiliaries proliferating; cells rebuilt from molecules; space colonized; population growth slackening; the world democratized; international trade accelerated; people better fed and healthier than ever before; life span stretched; religion holding firm.*

In this buoyant vision of the twenty-first century, what might we have overlooked about our place in history? What are we neglecting and at risk of forever losing? The answer most likely in the year 3000 is: *much of the rest of life, and part of what it means to be a human being.*

A few technophiles, I expect, will beg to differ. What, after all, in the long term does it mean to be human? We have traveled this far; we will go on. As to the rest of life, they continue, we should be able to immerse fertilized eggs and clonable tissues of endangered species in liquid nitrogen and use them later to rebuild the destroyed ecosystems. Even that may not be necessary: in time entirely new species and ecosystems, better suited to human needs than the old ones, can be created by genetic engineering. *Homo sapiens* might choose to redesign itself along the way, the better to live in a new biological order of our own making.

Such is the extrapolated endpoint of technomania applied to the natural world. The compelling response, in my opinion, is that to travel even partway there would be a dangerous gamble, a single throw of the dice with the future of life on the table. To revive or synthesize the thousands of species needed—probably millions when the still largely unknown microorganisms have been cataloged—and put them together in functioning ecosystems is beyond even the theoretical imagination of existing science. Each species is adapted to particular physical and chemical environments within the habitat. Each species has evolved to fit together with certain other species in ways biologists are only beginning to understand. To synthesize ecosystems on bare ground or in empty water is no more practicable than the reanimation of deep-frozen human corpses. And to redesign the human genotype better to fit a ruined biosphere is the stuff of science horror fiction. Let us leave it there, in the realm of imagination.

Another reason exists not to take the gamble, not to let the natural world slip away. Suppose, for the sake of argument, that new species can be engineered and stable ecosystems built from them. With that distant potential in mind, should we go ahead, and for short-term gain, allow the original species and ecosystems to slip away? Yes? Erase Earth's living history? Then also burn the libraries and art galleries, make cordwood of the musical instruments, pulp the musical scores, erase Shakespeare, Beethoven, and Goethe, and the Beatles too, because all these—or at least fairly good substitutes—can be re-created.

The issue, like all great decisions, is moral. Science and technology are what we can do; morality is what we agree we should or should not do. The ethic from which moral decisions spring is a norm or standard of behavior in support of a value, and value in turn depends on purpose. Purpose, whether personal or global, whether urged by conscience or graven in sacred script, expresses the image we hold of ourselves and our society. In short, ethics evolve through discrete steps, from self-image to purpose to value to ethical precepts to moral reasoning.

A conservation ethic is that which aims to pass on to future generations the best part of the nonhuman world. To know this world is to gain a proprietary attachment to it. To know it well is to love and take responsibility for it.

Each species—American eagle, Sumatran rhinoceros, flat-spined three-toothed land snail, furbish lousewort, and on down the roster of ten million or more still with us—is a masterpiece. The craftsman who assembled them was natural selection, acting upon mutations and recombinations of genes, through vast numbers of steps over long periods of time. Each species, when examined closely, offers an endless bounty of knowledge and aesthetic pleasure. It is a living library. The number of genes prescribing a eukaryotic life form such as a Douglas fir or a human being runs into the tens of thousands. The nucleotide pairs composing them—in other words, the genetic letters that encode the life-giving enzymes—vary among species from one billion to ten billion. If the DNA helics in one cell of a mouse, a typical animal species, were placed end on end and magically enlarged to have the same width as wrapping string, they would extend for over nine hundred kilometers, with about four thousand nucleotide pairs packed into every meter. Measured in bits of pure information, the genome of a cell is comparable to all editions of the *Encyclopedia Britannica* published since its inception in 1768.

The creature at your feet dismissed as a bug or a weed is a creation in and of itself. It has a name, a million year history, and a place in the world. Its genome adapts it to a special niche in an ecosystem. The ethical value substantiated by close examination of its biology is that the life forms around us are too old, too complex, and potentially too useful to be carelessly discarded.

Biologists point to another ethically potent value; the genetic unity of life. All organisms have descended from the same distant ancestral life form. The reading of the genetic codes has shown thus far that the common ancestor of all living species was similar to present-day bacteria and Achaeans, single-celled microbes with the simplest known anatomy and molecular composition. Because of this single ancestry, which arose on Earth over 3.5 billion years ago, all species today share certain fundamental molecular traits. Their tissue is divided into cells, whose enveloping lipid membranes regulate exchange with the outside environment. The molecular machinery that generates energy is similar. The genetic information is stored in DNA, transcribed into RNA, and translated into proteins. Finally, a large array of mostly similar protein catalysts, the enzymes, accelerate all the life processes.

Still another intensely felt value is stewardship, which appears to arise from emotions programmed in the very genes of human social behavior. Because all organisms have descended from a common ancestor, it is correct to say that the biosphere as a whole began to think when humanity was born. If the rest of life is the body, we are the mind. Thus, our place in nature, viewed from an ethical perspective, is to think about the creation and to protect the living planet.

mind body analogy

As cognitive scientists have focused on the nature of the mind, they have come to characterize it not just as a physical entity, the brain at work, but more specifically as a flood of scenarios. Whether set in the past, present, or future, whether based on reality or entirely fictive, these free-running narratives are all churned out with equal facility. The present is constructed from the avalanche of sensations that pour into the wakened brain. Working at a furious pace, the brain summons memories to screen and make sense of the incoming chaos. Only a minute part of the information is selected for higher-order processing. From that part, small segments are enlisted through symbolic imagery to create the white-hot core of activity we call the conscious mind.

During the story-building process the past is reworked and then returned to storage. The repeated cycles allow the brain to hold on to only small but shrinking fragments of these former conscious states. Over a lifetime the details of real events are increasingly distorted by editing and supplementation. Across generations the most important among them turn into history, and finally legend and myth.

Each culture has its own creation myth, the primary functions of which are to place the tribe that contrived it at the center of the universe, and to portray history as a noble epic. The ultimate epic unfolding through science is the genetic history both of *Homo sapiens* and of all our antecedents. Traced back far enough through time, across more than three billion years, all organisms on Earth share a common ancestry. That genetic unity is a fact-based history confirmed with increasing exactitude by the geneticists and paleontologists who reconstruct evolutionary genealogy. If *Homo sapiens* as a whole must have a creation myth—and emotionally in the age of globalization it seems we must—none is more solid and unifying for the species than evolutionary history. That is another value favoring stewardship of the natural world.

To summarize: a sense of genetic unity, kinship, and deep history are among the values that bond us to the living environment. They are survival mechanisms for ourselves and our species. To conserve biological diversity is an investment in immortality.

Do other species therefore have inalienable rights? There are three reaches of altruism possible from which a response can be made. The first is anthropocentrism: nothing matters except that which affects humanity. Then pathocentrism: intrinsic rights should be extended to chimpanzees, dogs, and other intelligent animals for whom we can legitimately feel empathy. And finally biocentrism: all kinds of organisms have an intrinsic right at least to exist. The three levels are not as exclusive as they first seem. In real life they often coincide, and when in life-or-death conflict, they can be ordered in priority as follows: first humanity, next intelligent animals, and then other forms of life.

The influence of the biocentric view, expressed institutionally through quasi-religious movements such as Deep Ecology and the Epic of Evolution, is growing worldwide. The philosopher Holmes Rolston III tells a story that can serve as a parable of this trend. For years, trailside signs at a sub alpine campground in the Rocky Mountains he occasionally visited read, "Please leave the flowers for others to enjoy." When the wooden signs began to erode and flake, they were replaced by new ones that read, "Let the flowers live!"

It is not so difficult to love nonhuman life, if gifted with knowledge about it. The capacity, even the proneness to do so, may well be one of the human instincts. The phenomenon has been called biophilia, defined as the innate tendency to focus upon life and lifelike forms, and in some instances to affiliate with them emotionally. Human beings sharply distinguish the living from the inanimate. We esteem novelty and diversity in other organisms. We are thrilled by the prospect of unknown creatures, whether in the deep sea, the unbroken forest, or remote mountains. We are riveted by the idea of life on other planets. Dinosaurs are our icons of vanished biodiversity. More people visit zoos in the United States than attend professional sports events. Their favorite site in the National Zoo of Washington, D.C., is the insect exhibit, representing maximum novelty and diversity.

A prominent component of biophilia is habitat selection. Studies conducted in the relatively new field of environmental psychology during the past thirty years point consistently to the following conclusion: people prefer to be in natural environments, and especially in savanna or park-like habitats. They like a long depth of view across a relatively smooth, grassy ground surface dotted with trees and copses. They want to be near a body of water, whether ocean, lake, river, or stream. They try to place their habitations on a prominence, from which they can safely scan the savanna and watery environment. With nearly absolute consistency, these landscapes are preferred over urban settings that are either bare or clothed in scant vegetation. To a relative degree people dislike woodland views that possess restricted depth of vision, a disordered complexity of vegetation, and rough ground structures—in short, forests with small, closely spaced trees and dense undergrowth. They want a topography and openings that improve their line of sight.

People prefer to look out over their ideal terrain from a secure position framed by the semi-enclosure of a domicile. Their choice of home and environs, if made freely, combines a balance of refuge for safety and a wide visual prospect for exploration and foraging. There may be small gender differences: among Western landscape painters at least, women stress refuges with small prospect spaces, and men stress large prospect spaces. Women also tend to place human figures in or near the refuges, while men place them more consistently in the open spaces beyond.

The ideal natural habitat is intuitively understood by landscape architects and real-estate entrepreneurs. Even when it offers no practical value, the setting commands a relatively high price, reaching its maximum if also located conveniently near cities.

I once described the principle of the ideal habitat to a wealthy friend as we looked down from his New York penthouse to the open woodland and lake of Central Park. His terrace, I also noticed, was ringed by potted plants. I thought of him as a convincing experimental subject. It has since often occurred to me that to see most clearly the manifestations of human instinct, it is useful to start with the rich, who among us enjoy the widest range of options in response, and most readily follow their emotional and aesthetic inclinations.

No direct evidence has yet been sought for a genetic basis of the human habitat preference, but its presence is suggested by a consistency in its manifestation across cultures, including those in North America, Europe, Korea, and Nigeria.

A similar convergence occurs in the aesthetics of tree form. Subjects in cross-cultural psychological tests prefer moderate-sized and sturdy trees with broad, layered canopies close to the ground. The species considered most attractive include acacias, which are dominant elements of healthy African savannas.

Tree aesthetics brings us to the question of the origin of the biophilic instincts. The human habitat preference is consistent with the "savanna hypothesis," that humanity originated in the savannas and transitional forests of Africa. Almost the full evolutionary history of the genus *Homo*, including *Homo sapiens* and its immediate ancestors, was spent in or near these habitats or others similar to them. If that amount of time, about two millions years, were to be compressed into a span of seventy years, humanity occupied the ancestral environment for sixty-nine years and eight months, whereupon some of the populations took up agriculture and moved into villages to spend the last 120 days.

The savanna hypothesis extended to include behavior stipulates that *Homo sapiens* is likely to be genetically specialized for the ancestral environment so that today, even in the most sequestered stone-and-glass cities, we still prefer it. Part of human nature is a residue of bias in mental development that causes us to gravitate back to savannas or their surrogates.

The savanna hypothesis of habitat preference may strike some readers as evolutionism run amok. But is the idea really so strange? Not at all: just a glance at the world of animal behavior suggests otherwise. Every species that moves under its own power, from protozoans to chimpanzees, instinctively seeks the habitat it must occupy in order to survive and reproduce. The behavioral steps for which it is genetically programmed are usually complex and exactly executed. The study of habitat selection is an important branch of ecology, and no species ever lets down the researcher who chooses to examine this part of its life cycle. To take one of a multitude of excellent examples, the African mosquito *Anopheles gambiae* is a species specialized to feed on human blood. (As a result it is a carrier of the malignant malarial parasite *Plasmodium falciparum.*) Each female, in order to complete her life cycle, finds her way from the stagnant pool of her birth and larval growth to a nearby village. In the daytime she hides in crevices of the house. At night she flies directly to one of the inhabitants, moving upwind through a plume of the chemically distinctive odor of the human body. She accomplishes all this with no experience and a brain the size of a grain of salt.

So it should be no great surprise that human beings, a biological species dependent on certain natural environments until very recently in its evolutionary history, should retain an aesthetic preference for savannas and transitional woodland among an array of natural and artificial environments laid before them. In general, what we call aesthetics may be just the pleasurable sensations we get from the particular stimuli to which our brains are inherently adapted.

To say that there is an instinct, or more accurately an array of instincts, that can be labeled biophilia is not to imply that the brain is hardwired. We do not ambulate like robots to the nearest lakeshore meadow. Instead, the brain is predisposed to acquire certain preferences as opposed to others. Psychologists who study mental development say that we are hereditarily *prepared* to learn certain behaviors and *counter-prepared* to learn others. The vast majority of humans, to use a familiar example, are prepared to learn the lyrics of a song but counter-prepared to learn calculus. We delight in the first and are fearful and begrudging of the second. Also, true to the pattern of instinct thus broadly defined, there are sensitive periods during childhood and early maturity in which learning and distaste are most easily picked up. In a manner also true to the conception, the timing varies among categories of behavior. Fluency in language comes earlier than fluency in mathematics.

The critical stages in the acquisition of biophilia have been worked out by psychologists during studies of childhood mental development. Under the age of six, children tend to be egocentric, self-serving, and domineering in their responses to animals and nature. They are also most prone to be uncaring or fearful of the natural world and of all but a few familiar animals. Between six and nine, children become interested in wild creatures for the first time, and aware that animals can suffer pain and distress. From nine to twelve their knowledge and interest in the natural world rises sharply, and between thirteen and seventeen they readily acquire moral feeling toward animal welfare and species conservation.

A single study in the United States devoted to the subject suggests that a parallel sequence unfolds in the development of habitat preference. Children between the ages of eight and eleven, when given a choice of environmental photographs spread before them, favored savanna over hardwood forest, north-temperate conifer forest, rainforest, and desert. In contrast, older children preferred hardwood forest and savanna equally—in other words, habitats with which they had the most direct experience during their adolescence. Both of these environments were chosen over the remaining three. From this one set of data at least, the evidence supports the savanna hypothesis. In other words, children are evidently predisposed to favor the ancestral human habitat, but then increasingly favor the environment in which they have grown up.

Another sequence occurs in the way children explore the environment. At four they confine themselves to the immediate vicinity of their home and to small creatures readily found there, the "worms, chipmunks and pigeons" of neighboring yards and streets, as David Sobel expressed it in *Children's Special Places*. At eight to eleven they head for nearby woods, fields, ditches, and other unclaimed spots they can claim as their own. There they often build some kind of shelter such as a tree house, fort, or cave where they can read magazines, eat lunch, conspire with a friend or two, play games, and spy on the world. If natural wild environments are available, so much the better, but they are not essential. In urban East Harlem, children were observed building forts in culverts, alleyways, basements, abandoned warehouses, railroad right-of-ways, and hedges.

The secret places of childhood, whether a product of instinct or not, at the very least predispose us to acquire certain preferences and to undertake practices of later value in survival. The hideaways bond us with place, and they nourish our individuality and self-esteem. They enhance joy in the construction of habitation. If played out in natural environments, they also bring us close to the earth and nature in ways that can engender a lifelong love of both. Such was my own experience as a boy of eleven to thirteen, when I sought little Edens in the forest of Alabama and Florida. On one occasion I built a small hut of saplings in a remote off-trail spot. Unfortunately, I didn't notice until later that some of the saplings were poison oak, a virulent relative of poison ivy. That was the last of my secret-house constructions, but my love of the natural world nevertheless grew even stronger.

If biophilia is truly part of human nature, if it is truly an instinct, we should be able to find evidence of a positive effect of the natural world and other organisms on health. In fact, the annals of physiology and medicine contain abundant and diverse studies affirming just such a connection, at least when health is broadly defined, to use the words of the World Health Organization, as "a state of complete physical, mental and social well-being and not merely the absence of disease and infirmity." The following results of published studies are representative:

- A population of 120 volunteers were shown a stressful movie, followed by videotapes of either natural or urban settings. By their own subjective rating, they recovered from the feeling of stress more quickly while experiencing the natural settings. Their opinion was supported by four standard physiological measures of stress: heartbeat, systolic blood pressure, facial muscle tension, and electrical skin conductance. The results suggest, although don't prove, the involvement of the parasympathetic nerves, that part of the autonomic system whose activation induces a state of relaxed awareness. The same result was obtained in a different group of student volunteers stressed by a difficult mathematical examination, and then shown videotapes that stimulated automobile rides through natural as opposed to urban settings.

- Studies of response prior to surgery and dental work have consistently revealed a significant reduction of stress in the presence of plants and aquaria. Natural environments viewed through windows or merely displayed in wall-mounted pictures produce the same effect.
- Post-surgical patients recover more quickly, suffer fewer minor complications, and need smaller dosages of painkillers if given a window view of open terrain or waterscape.
- In one Swedish study covering fifteen years of records, clinically anxious psychiatric patients responded positively to wall pictures of natural environments, but negatively, occasionally even violently, to most other decorations (especially those containing abstract art).
- Comparable studies in prisons revealed that inmates provided window views of nearby farmlands and forest, as opposed to prison yards, reported fewer stress-related symptoms such as headaches and indigestion.
- In a different category, the popular notion that owning pets reduces stress-related problems has been well supported by research conducted independently in Australia, England, and the United States. In one Australian study, which factored out variation in exercise levels, diet, and social class, pet ownership accounted for a statistically significant reduction of cholesterol, triglycerides, and systolic blood pressure. In a parallel U.S. study, survivors of heart attacks (myocardial infarction) who owned dogs had a survival rate six times higher than those who did not. The same benefit was not, I am sorry to report, enjoyed by cat owners.

The implications of biophilia for preventive medicine are substantial. The biophilic instinct can be counted as one of humanity's fortunate irrationalities, like women's choice to have fewer children when economically secure, that deserve to be understood better and put to more practical use. It is a remarkable fact that while average life expectancy in the leading industrialized countries has risen to nearly eighty years, the contribution of preventive medicine, including the design of healthful and curative environments, has remained far below potential. Obesity, diabetes, melanoma, asthma, depression, hip fracture, and breast cancer have risen in frequency since 1980. Further, despite advances in scientific knowledge and public awareness, neither coronary atherosclerosis among young people nor acute myocardial infarction among the middle-ages and old has declined. All of these conditions can be delayed or even avoided by preventive measures that include, in most cases and to the point I wish to make, a reconnection to the natural world. As such they are cost-effective, amounting to no more than salvage of natural habitats, improvements in landscape design, and relocation of windows in public buildings.

Of course nature has a dark side too. The face it presents to humanity is not always friendly. Throughout most of human deep history there have been predators eager to snatch us for dinner; venomous snakes ready with a fatal, defensive strike to the ankle; spiders and insects that bite, sting, and infect; and microbes designed to reduce the human body to malodorous catabolic chemicals. The reverse side of nature's green-and-gold is the black-and-scarlet of disease and death. The companion of biophilia is therefore biophobia. Like the responses of biophilia, those of biophobia are acquired by prepared learning. They vary in intensity among individuals according to heredity and experience. At one end of the scale are mild distaste and feelings of apprehension. At the other end are full-blown clinical phobias that fire the sympathetic nervous system and produce panic, nausea, and cold sweat. The innate biophobic intensities are most readily evoked by sources of peril that have existed in the natural world throughout humanity's evolutionary past. They include heights, close spaces, running water, snakes, wolves, rats and mice, bats, spiders, and blood. In contrast, prepared learning is unknown in response to knives, frayed electric wires, automobiles, and guns, although far deadlier today than the ancient perils of humankind, are too recent in evolutionary history to have been targeted by genetically prepared learning.

The defining properties of hereditary predisposition are multiple. One negative experience may be enough to trigger the response and permanently instill the fear. The critical stimulus can be unexpected and very simple—for example, the abrupt approach of an animal face, or the writhing of a serpent or serpent-like object nearby. The likelihood of imprinting is enhanced by already existing stressful conditions that surround the event. The learning can even be vicarious: just witnessing panic in another person or listening to a scary story can induce it in some people.

Those in whom the fear has been implanted respond almost instantly and subconsciously to subliminal images. When psychologists flashed pictures of snakes or spiders to subjects for only fifteen to thirty milliseconds, intervals too brief to be processed by the conscious mind, those previously conditioned adversely to these animals reacted with automatic muscle changes in the face within less than half a second. Although the response was easily detectable by the researchers, the subjects remained unaware that anything had happened at all.

Because aversive responses are so well defined, it has been possible to apply standard tests used in human genetics to determine whether variation in them among people has at least a partly genetic basis. The measure of choice is heritability, the standard used in studies of personality, obesity, neuroticism, and other traits that display complex variation in human populations. Heritability of a given trait is the percentage of variation among individuals in a population due to differences in genes among the individuals, as opposed to the percentage caused by differences in their environment. The heritability of innate aversion to snakes, spiders, insects, and bats respectively has been estimated to be about 30 percent, a common figure for human behavioral traits in general. The heritability of proneness to agoraphobia, an extreme aversion to crowds or open areas, is about 40 percent.

Another characteristic of prepared aversion is the existence of a sensitive period, which as in biophilic behavior is the interval in the normal life cycle when learning is easiest and the trait most apt to be established. In the case of ophidiophobia (snake), arachnophobia (spider), and other animal phobias, the onset occurs during childhood, with about 70 percent of cases occurring by ten years of age. In contrast, agoraphobia is an affliction of adolescents and young adults, triggered in 60 percent of the cases between fifteen and thirty years of age.

If elements of the natural world can sometimes paralyze modern humans by the evocation of ancient instincts, human instinct can and does wreak havoc on the natural world. Finding themselves surrounded by forests that once covered most of Earth's habitable land, Neolithic peoples set out ten thousand years ago to convert them into cropland, pasture, corrals, and scattered woodlots. What they could not chop down, they burned. Successive generations, their populations growing, continued the process until today only half the original cover is left. They needed the food, of course, but there is another way of looking at the relentless deforestation. People then as now instinctively wanted the ancestral habitat. So they proceeded to create savanna crafted to human needs. *Homo sapien* did not evolve to be a forest dweller, like chimpanzees, gorillas, and other great apes. Rather, it became a specialist of open spaces. The aesthetically ideal environment of today's transformed world is the much-treasured pastoral landscape, for better or worse our ersatz savanna.

Where does attachment to that habitat leave wilderness? No question in environmental ethics cuts more deeply. Before agriculture and villages were invented, people lived in or very close to nature. They were part of it, and had no need for the concept of wilderness. Pastoral settlers drew a line between cultivated and virgin land. As they pushed back virgin land and built more complex societies with the aid of agricultural surpluses, they sharpened the distinction. Those in more advanced cultures imagined themselves to be above the untamed world around them. They were destined, they thought, to dwell among the gods. The word "wilderness" acquired the meaning expressed in its Old English progenitor *wil(d)dēornes:* wild, savage. To pastoral and urban sensibilities, it was the impenetrable dark woods, the mountain fastness, the thorn bush desert, the open sea, and any other part of the world that had not been and might never be tamed. It was the realm of beasts, savages, evil spirits, magic, and the menacing, amorphous unknown.

The European conquest of the New World established the concept of wilderness as a frontier region waiting to be rolled back. The image was most clearly formed in the United States, whose early history is geographically defined as a westward march across an undeveloped and fertile continent.

Then came a tipping point. By the time the American frontier closed, around 1890, wilderness had become a scarce resource at risk of being eliminated altogether and hence worth saving. American environmentalism was born, rising upon the new conservation ethic created by Henry David Thoreau, John Muir, and other nineteenth-century prophets. It spread slowly through the United States, Europe, and elsewhere. It argued that humanity would be foolish to wager its future on a wholly transformed planet. Wild lands in particular, the early environmentalists said, have a unique value for humankind. The warrior king of the movement was Theodore Roosevelt, who declared, "I hate a man who skins the land."

What is a wilderness today in our largely humanized world? What it has always been: a space that sustains itself, was here before humanity, and where, in the words of the Wilderness Act of 1964, "the Earth and its community of life are untrammeled by man and where man himself is a visitor who does not remain." The true great wildernesses of the world include the rainforests of the Amazon, the Congo, and New Guinea; the evergreen coniferous forests of northern North America and Eurasia; and Earth's ancient deserts, polar regions, and open seas.

A few contrarians like to claim that true wilderness is a thing of the past. They point out, correctly, that very few places on land have remained untrodden by human feet. Moreover, 5 percent of Earth's land surface is burned every year, and the plumes of nitrous oxide produced travel most of the way around the world. Greenhouse gases thicken, global temperatures rise, and glaciers and montane forests retreat up mountain peaks. With the exception of a few places in tropical Asia and Africa, terrestrial environments everywhere have lost most of their largest mammals, birds, and reptiles, destabilizing the populations of many other kinds of plants and animals. As the remnant wild areas shrink, they are invaded by more and more alien species, diminishing the native plants and animals yet more. The smaller the area of the natural reserves, the more we are forced to intervene to avoid the partial collapse of their ecosystems.

All true. But to claim that the surviving wildernesses are less than the name implies, and have in some sense become part of the human domain, is false. The argument is specious. It is like flattening the Himalayas to the level of the Ganges Delta by saying that all the planet's surface is but a geometer's plane. Walk from a pasture into a tropical rainforest, sail from a harbor marina to a coral reef, and you will see the difference. The glory of the primeval world is still there to protect and savor.

The exact perception of wilderness is a matter of scale. Even in disturbed environments, with most of their native plants and vertebrates long vanished, bacteria, protozoans, and miniature invertebrates still maintain the ancient substratum. The micro-wildernesses are more accessible than full-scale wildernesses. They are usually only minutes away, waiting to be visited by microscope instead of jetliner. A single tree in a city park, harboring thousands of species, is an island, complete with miniature mountains, valleys, lakes, and subterranean caverns. Scientists have only begun to explore these compacted worlds. Educators have made surprisingly little use of them in introducing the wonders of life to students. Micro aesthetics based upon them is still an unexplored wilderness to the creative mind.

A strong case can be made for the creation of micro-reserves. A one-hectare patch of rainforest still clinging to a Honduran hillside, a road strip of native grasses in Iowa, and a muddy natural pond on the edge of a Florida golf course are to be valued and preserved even if the large native organisms that once lived in and around them have disappeared.

Still, while micro-reserves are infinitely better than nothing at all, they are no substitute for macro- and mega-reserves, where full-blown biotas with sizable animals continue to live. People can acquire an appreciation for savage carnivorous nematodes and shape-shifting rotifers in a drop of pond water, but they need life on the large scale to which the human intellect and emotion most naturally respond. No one of my acquaintance, except a few microbiologists, would visit a town dump upon being told it harbors a dazzling variety of bacteria. But tourists and locals alike travel to the dumps of sub-arctic Canadian towns to watch scavenging polar bears.

To the multiple valorizations of wild environments can be added mystery. Without mystery life shrinks. The completely known is a numbing void to all active minds. Even a laboratory rat seeks the advantage of the maze.

So we are drawn to the natural world, aware that it contains structure and complexity and length of history as well, at orders of magnitude greater than anything yet conceived in human imagination. Mysteries solved within it merely uncover more mysteries beyond. For the naturalist every entrance into a wild environment rekindles an excitement that is childlike in spontaneity, often tinged with apprehension—in short, the way life ought to be lived, all the time.

I will offer one such personal remembrance out of hundreds forever fresh in my mind. It is the summer of 1965, in the Dry Tortugas, at the tip of the Florida Keys. I stand at the water's edge on Garden Key, with Fort Jefferson at my back, looking across a narrow channel to Bush Key, where the littoral scrub and mangrove swamp are alive with thousands of nesting sooty terns. I have a boat, and I will go there soon, but right now I have an inexplicable urge to swim across instead. The channel is about a hundred feet across, maybe less, and the tidal current from the Gulf of Mexico to Florida Bay is for the moment too slow to pose a risk. There will be no problem if I choose to swim, it seems. Then I look more closely at the moving water. How deep is the channel center? What might come up from below to meet me? A barracuda? I saw a five-footer circling the nearby dock pilings that morning. And what do I know about the local sharks? Hammerheads and bull sharks are common in deeper water, for sure, and have been known to attack humans. Great whites are occasionally seen. Shark attacks in this region are very rare, yet—would I be the dramatic exception? Now, reflecting as I hesitate, I feel an urge not just to cross, but to dive and explore the bottom of the channel. I want to know it inch by inch as I know the soil surface of the islands I have been studying, to see what else lives there and comes in sporadically from the Gulf.

The impulse to swim fades as quickly as it arose, but I make a resolution to come back someday and become an intimate of the channel and its inhabitants and to bond with this place on which I have randomly fixated, to make it part of my life. There is something crazy about the episode, but also something real, primal, and deeply satisfying.

At some time in our lives—for the naturalist always—we long for the gate to the paradisiacal world. It is the instinctive after-image that comes to us in daydreams, and a wellspring of hope. Its mysteries, if ignited in our minds and solved, grant more control over existence. If ignored, they leave an emotional void. How did such a strange quality of human nature come about? No one knows for sure, but evolutionary genetics tells us that even if just one person in a thousand survived because of a genetic predisposition to explore the unknown and persevere in daunting circumstances, then over many generations, natural selection would have installed the predisposition in the whole human race to wonder and take the dare.

We need nature, and particularly its wilderness strongholds. It is the alien world that gave rise to our species, and the home to which we can safely return. It offers choices our spirit was designed to enjoy.

Wilson writes that "micro-wildernesses are more accessible than full-scale wildernesses. They are usually only minutes away, waiting to be visited by the microscope instead of jetliner." By way of example, Wilson likens a single tree in a city park to an island. With this metaphor in mind, explore your campus, your back yard, or a local park, forest, or lake. What micro-wildernesses make up your local environment? As a class, develop a list of these locations and discuss how they might introduce you and others to what Wilson characterizes as "the wonders of life."

Wilson cites the World Health Organization's definition of health: "a state of complete physical, mental, and social well-being and not merely the absence of disease and infirmity." According to Wilson, how does biophilia promote this state of being? What do you think is the environment's role in promoting the health of humans?

Collaborate

In his piece, Wilson recounts philosopher Holmes Rolston III's telling of a brief story: "For years, trailside signs at a sub alpine campground in the Rocky Mountains ... read, 'Please leave the flowers for others to enjoy.' When the wooden signs began to erode and flake, they were replaced by new ones that read, 'Let the flowers live!'" Working with a small group, discuss this story and its meaning, and decide how Wilson uses it to explain the nature of biocentrism.

In these excerpts from her 1999 memoir Ecology of a Cracker Childhood, *author and environmental activist Janisse Ray writes eloquently of her family's deep-rooted ties to the longleaf pine forests of southern Georgia and of her fears about the destruction of these irreplaceable ecosystems.*

excerpts from

ECOLOGY OF A CRACKER CHILDHOOD

BY JANISSE RAY

INTRODUCTION

In south Georgia everything is flat and wide. Not empty. My people live among the mobile homes, junked cars, pine plantations, clearcuts, and fields. They live among the lost forests.

The creation ends in south Georgia, at the very edge of the sweet earth. Only the sky, widest of the wide, goes on, flatness a gainst flatness. The sky appears so close that, with a long-enough extension ladder, you think you could touch it, and sometimes you do, when clouds descend in the night to set a fine pelt of dew on the grasses, leaving behind white trails of fog and mist.

At night the stars are thick and bright as a pint jar of fireflies, the moon at full a pearly orb, sailing through them like an egret. By day the sun, close in a paper sky, laps moisture from the land, then gives it back, always an exchange. Even in drought, when each dawn a parched sun cracks against the horizon's griddle, the air is thick with water.

It is a land of few surprises. It is a land of routine, of cycle, and of constancy. Many a summer afternoon a black cloud builds to the southwest, approaching until you hear thunder and spot lightning, and even then there's time to clear away tools and bring in the laundry before the first raindrops spatter down. Everything that comes you see coming.

That's because the land is so wide, so much of it open. It's wide open, flat as a book, vulnerable as a child. It's easy to take advantage of, and yet it is also a land of dignity. It has been the way it is for thousands of years, and it is not wont to change.

I was born from people who were born from people who were born from people who were born here. The Crackers crossed the wide Altamaha into what had been Creek territory and settled the vast, fire-loving uplands of the coastal plains of southeast Georgia, surrounded by a singing forest of tall and widely spaced pines whose history they did not know, whose stories were untold. The memory of what they entered is scrawled on my bones, so that I carry the landscape inside like an ache. The story of who I am cannot be severed from the story of the flatwoods.

To find myself among what has been and what remains, I go where my grandmother's name is inscribed on a clay hill beside my grandfather. The cemetery rests in a sparse stand of remnant longleaf pine, where clumps of wiregrass can still be found. From the grave I can see a hardwood drain, hung with Spanish moss, and beyond to a cypress swamp, and almost to the river, but beyond that, there is only sky.

CHILD OF PINE

When my parents had been married five years and my sister was four, they went out searching among the pinewoods through which the junkyard had begun to spread. It was early February of 1962, and the ewes in the small herd of sheep that kept the grass cropped around the junked cars were dropping lambs.

On this day, Candlemas, with winter half undone, a tormented wind bore down from the north and brought with it a bitter wet cold that cut through my parents' sweaters and coats and sliced through thin socks, stinging their skin and penetrating to the bone. Tonight the pipes would freeze if the faucets weren't left dripping, and if the fig tree wasn't covered with quilts, it would be knocked back to the ground.

It was dark by six, for the days lengthened only by minutes, and my father had gone early to shut up the sheep. Nights he penned them in one end of his shop, a wide, tin-roofed building that smelled both acrid and sweet, a mixture of dry dung, gasoline, hay, and grease. That night when he counted them, one of the ewes was missing. He had bought the sheep to keep weeds and snakes down in the junkyard, so people could get to parts they needed; now he knew all the animals by name and knew also their personalities. Maude was close to her time.

In the hour they had been walking, the temperature had fallen steadily. It would soon be dark. Out of the grayness Mama heard a bleating cry.

"Listen," she said, touching Daddy's big arm and stopping so suddenly that shoulder-length curls of dark hair swung across her heart-shaped face. Her eyes were a deep, rich brown, and she cut a fine figure, slim and strong, easy in her body. Her husband was over six feet tall, handsome, his forehead wide and smart, his hair thick and wiry as horsetail.

Again came the cry. It sounded more human than sheep, coming from a clump of palmettos beneath a pine. The sharp-needled fronds of the palmettos stood out emerald against the gray of winter, and the pine needles, so richly brown when first dropped, had faded to dull sienna. Daddy slid his hands—big, rough hands—past the bayonet-tipped palmetto fronds, their fans rattling urgently with his movements, him careful not to rake against saw-blade stems. The weird crying had not stopped. He peered in.

It was a baby. Pine needles cradled a long-limbed newborn child with a duff of dark hair, its face red and puckered. And that was me, his second-born. I came into their lives easy as finding a dark-faced merino with legs yet too wobbly to stand.

My sister had been found in a big cabbage in the garden; a year after me, my brother was discovered under the grapevine, and a year after that, my little brother appeared beside a huckleberry bush. From as early as I could question, I was told this creation story. If they'd said they'd found me in the trunk of a '52 Ford, it would have been more believable. I was raised on a junkyard on the outskirts of a town called Baxley, the county seat of Appling, in rural south Georgia. [...]

BELOW THE FALL LINE

The landscape that I was born to, that owns my body: the uplands and lowlands of southern Georgia. The region lies below what's called the fall line, a half-imaginary demarcation avouched by a slight dip in the land, above which the piedmont climbs to the foothills of the Blue Ridge, then up that mountain chain to the eastern continental divide. The fall line separates the piedmont from the Atlantic coastal plain—a wide flat plateau of piney-woods that sweeps to a marble sea.

My homeland is about as ugly as a place gets. There's nothing in south Georgia, people will tell you, except straight, lonely roads, one-horse towns, sprawling farms, and tracts of planted pines. It's flat, monotonous, used-up, hotter than hell in summer and cold enough in winter that orange trees won't grow. No mountains, no canyons, no rocky streams, no waterfalls. The rivers are muddy, wide and flat, like somebody's feet. The coastal plain lacks the stark grace of the desert or the umber panache of the pampas. Unless you look close, there's little majesty.

It wasn't always this way. Even now, in places, in the Red Hills near Thomasville, for example, and on Fort Stewart Military Reservation near Hinesville, you can see how south Georgia used to be, before all the old longleaf pine forests that were our sublimity and our majesty were cut. Nothing is more beautiful, nothing more mysterious, nothing more breathtaking, nothing more surreal.

Longleaf pine is the tree that grows in the upland flatwoods of the coastal plains. Miles and miles of longleaf and wiregrass, the ground cover that coevolved with the pine, once covered the left hip of North America—from Virginia to the Florida peninsula, west past the Mississippi River: longleaf as far in any direction as you could see. In a longleaf forest, miles of trees forever fade into a brilliant salmon sunset and reappear the next dawn as a battalion marching out of fog. The tip of each needle carries a single drop of silver. The trees are so well spaced that their limbs seldom touch and sunlight streams between and within them. Below their flattened branches, grasses arch their tall, richly dun heads of seeds, and orchids and lilies paint the ground orange and scarlet. Purple liatris gestures across the landscape. Our eyes seek the flowers like they seek the flash of birds and the careful crossings of forest animals.

You can still see this in places.

Forest historians estimate that longleaf covered 85 of the 156 million acres in its southeastern range. By 1930, virtually all of the virgin longleaf pine had been felled. Now, at the end of the twentieth century, about two million acres of longleaf remain. Most is first-and second-growth, hard-hit by logging, turpentining, grazing, and the suppression of fire.

Less than 10,000 acres are virgin—not even 0.001 percent of what was. There's none known in Virginia, none in Louisiana, non in Texas, none in South Carolina. About 200 old-growth acres remain in Mississippi, about 300 in Alabama, and almost 500 in North Carolina, in four separate tracts. The rest survives in Georgia and Florida. An estimated 3,000 acres of old-growth in Georgia lie on private land, precariously, and the largest holding of virgin longleaf, about 5,000 acres, belongs to Eglin Air Force Base in Florida.

In a 1995 National Biological Service assessment of biological loss, ecologist Reed Noss classified the longleaf/wiregrass community as "critically endangered." Ninety-eight percent of the presettlement longleaf pine barrens in the southeastern coastal plains were lost by 1986, he said. Natural stands—meaning not planted—have been reduced by about 99 percent.

Apocalyptic.

This was not a loss I knew as a child. *Longleaf* was a word I never heard. But it is a loss that as an adult shadows every step I take. I am daily aghast at how much we have taken, since it does not belong to us, and how much as a people we have suffered in consequence.

Not long ago I dreamed of actually cradling a place, as if something so amorphous and vague as a region, existing mostly in imagination and idea, suddenly took form. I held its shrunken relief in my arms, a baby smelted from a plastic topography map, and when I gazed down into its face, as my father had gazed into mine, I saw the pine flatwoods of my homeland.

CLEARCUT

If you clear a forest, you'd better pray continuously. While you're pushing a road through and rigging the cables and moving between trees on the dozer, you'd better be talking to God. While you're cruising timber and marking trees with a blue slash, be praying; and pray while you're peddling the chips and logs and writing Friday's checks and paying the diesel bill—even if it's under your breath, a rustling at the lips. If you're manning the saw head or the scissors, snipping the trees off at the ground, going from one to another, approaching them brusquely and laying them down, I'd say, pray extra hard; and pray hard when you're hauling them away.

God doesn't like a clearcut. It makes his heart turn cold, makes him wince and wonder what went wrong with his creation, and sets him to thinking about what spoils the child.

You'd better be pretty sure that the cut is absolutely necessary and be at peace with it, so you can explain it to God, for it's fairly certain he's going to question your motives, want to know if your children are hungry and your oldest boy needs asthma medicine—whether you deserve forgiveness or if you're being greedy and heartless. You'd better pay good attention to the saw blade and the runners and the falling trees; when a forest is falling, it's easy for God to determine to spank. Quid pro quo.

Don't ever look away or daydream and don't, no matter what, plan how you will spend your tree money while you are in among toppling trees.

For a long time God didn't worry about the forests. Some trees got cut, which was bad enough, of course, and he would be sick about the cutting awhile, but his children needed houses and warmth, so he stepped in right after they had gone and got some seeds in the ground. The clear-cutting had come so fast he'd been unprepared. One minute the loggers were axmen, with their crosscut saws and oxen and rafts, and when he looked again, they were in helicopters.

When people started to replant, it was a good thing, but there was no way to re-create a forest. Not quickly. And the trees would just be cut again.

Before God knew it, his trees were being planted in rows, like corn, and harvested like corn. That was 1940, when the tree farming started, but it seems like yesterday to God.

Not longleaf. It was quirky in habit, its taproot cumbersome to deal with and slow-growing, so most of the tree farmers abandoned it. They could plant slash or loblolly and in twenty-five years be able to cut again.

Plant for the future, the signs said.

To prepare ground, they chopped, disked, rootraked, herbicided, windrowed. In wetter soils they bedded, plowing and heaping the soil into wide racks with drainage furrows between. The land was laid bare as a vulture's pate, and the scriveners came on their tree-planting tractors, driving down new words to replace the old one, *forest*.

The trees were planted close, five or six feet between, in phalanxes. They were all the same age and size, unlike the woodland that had been, with its old-growth and its saplings, as well as every age in between. The old forest had snags where woodpeckers fed and it had pine cones eager to burst open on bare ground.

Because slash and loblolly are intolerant of fire, the tree farmers, with Smokey as mascot, kept fire back. Within ten years a canopy would close, and the commercial plantation was dark within, darker than you can imagine a forest being. The limbs and needles of the overcrowded pines drank every inch of sky. Any native vegetation that survived land preparation did not survive loss of light.

The diversity of the forest decreased exponentially the more it was altered. In autumn, the flatwoods salamander no longer crossed the plantation to breed, and the migrating redstart no longer stopped, and the pine snake was not to be found. The gopher frog was a thirsty pool of silence.

Pine plantations dishearten God. In them he aches for blooming things, and he misses the sun trickling through the tree crowns, and he pines for the crawling, spotted, scale-backed, bushy-tailed, leaf-hopping, chattering creatures. Most of all he misses the bright-winged, singing beings he cast as angels.

The wind knocking limbs together is a jeremiad.

God likes to prop himself against a tree in a forest and study the plants and animals. They all please him. He has to drag himself through a pine plantation, looking for light on the other side, half-crazy with darkness, half-sick with regret. He refuses to go into clearcuts at all. He thought he had given his children everything their hearts would desire; what he sees puts him in a quarrelsome mood, wondering where he went wrong.

Ray characterizes herself as a "child of pine" and re-tells the "creation stories" told to her and her sister about how they came into the world. What are these "creation stories" and why do you think Ray includes them in her memoir? What do they tell you about her? How do these make her message more concrete and compelling?

Compose

Ray explains that her Georgia homeland "is about as ugly as a place gets," but that "[i]t wasn't always that way." With Ray's descriptions of the now disappearing longleaf pines in mind, write a eulogy for a vanished environment in which you use thoughtful plotting and vivid description to bring to life a place that was important to you in some way. For example, you could write a eulogy for local farmland that has been developed, for a tree that's been knocked over in a storm, or for the lake house where you vacationed with your parents. The idea is to remember and mourn a place that no longer exists for you. This "vanishing" can be tangible (like a once pristine beach that has been lost to erosion) or it can be emotional (like your childhood home, which, though still standing, is no longer the place it was to you then).

Collaborate

Ray describes her south Georgia home like this: "At night the stars are thick and bright as a pint jar of fireflies, the moon at full a pearly orb, sailing through them like an egret. By day the sun, close in a paper sky, laps moisture from the land, then gives it back, always an exchange. Even in drought, when each dawn a parched sun cracks against the horizon's griddle, the air is thick with water." As part of a group, come up with a highly descriptive account of your own home environment and then imitate Ray's evocative passage. You might even borrow Ray's night-and-day structure. Discuss with your group members how best to model the rich, sensual language she employs, incorporating not only visual descriptions but also elements of sound and touch that characterize your natural space.

The irreverent and infamous graffiti artist known as Banksy created this poster—featuring iconic Disney characters from the 1967 film *Jungle Book*—for the environmental organization Greenpeace, as part of a campaign against deforestation. It was also made into stickers and included in the 2006 book called *Banksy: Wall and Piece.* You can see more of Banksy's work at http://www.banksy.co.uk/. Turn the page for writing and discussion prompts focusing on this image.

Using the internet, find out more about both Banksy and Greenpeace. After conducting this research, explain why you think Greenpeace would use the work of an artist like Banksy to help advance its causes.

Based on the content of the Jungle Book image that Banksy produced, (see page 35) who do you think is the poster's intended audience? Who might Greenpeace be trying to reach with this particular text? What messages does the poster convey? Do you think this text presents an effective argument?

Working with a group of classmates, find another example of a pop culture icon (this can include fictional characters, celebrities, sports figures, and the like) being used to advance a social or political cause. Discuss with your group why you think this particular icon was matched with the issue at hand. Do you think this pairing was effective? Was it persuasive? Explain your responses.

Study the Banksy poster on page 35 and the "Denali/Denial" image by artist Chris Jordan on page 81. Then, write a brief essay in which you compare and evaluate the two pieces as visual arguments about the environment. In your essay, you should consider the purpose and intended audience for each piece, as well as each work's ability to connect with that audience. In the end, you should determine which image you find to be more persuasive and explain why.

Michelle Cliff—the author of novels, prose poetry, and works of criticism—was born in Jamaica and grew up there and in the United States. "Obsolete Geography" is part of the 1985 collection The Land of Look Behind. *"The landscapes that are important to me are those that I have internalized," she said in a 2010 interview with* Lambda Literary. *"Certainly my homeland of Jamaica, the photographic impressions of childhood, the witnessing of great natural beauty and great human tragedy. I always wanted to know why these two things coexisted—naive perhaps but then I was a child."*

OBSOLETE GEOGRAPHY

By Michelle Cliff

I

Airplane shadows moved across the mountains, leaving me to clear rivers, dancing birds, sweet fruits. Sitting on a river rock, my legs dangle in the water. I am twelve—and solitary.

II

On a hillside I search for mangoes. As I shake the tree the fruit drops: its sweetness splits at my feet. I suck the remaining flesh from the hairy seed. The sap from the stem stains my lips—to fester later. I am warned I may be scarred.

III

My other life of notebooks, lessons, homework continues. I try not to pay it mind.

IV

Things that live here: star apple, pineapple, custard apple, south sea apple; tamarind, ginep, avocado, guava, cashew, cane; yellow, white, St. Vincent yam; red, black, pepper ants; bats, scorpions, nightingales, spiders; cassava, sweetsop, soursop, cho-cho, okra, guango, mahoe, mahogany, ackee, plaintain, chinese banana; poly lizard, green lizard, croaking lizard, ground lizard.

V

The pig is big, and hangs suspended by her hind legs from a tree in the yard. She is screaming—her agony not self conscious. I have been told not to watch her slaughter, but my twelve-year-old self longs for the flow of blood. A small knife is inserted in her throat, pulled back, and forth until the throat slits, the wound widens, and blood runs over, covering the yard.

As her cries cease, mine begin. I have seen other slaughters but this one will stay with me.

VI

My grandmother's verandah before they renovated the house sloped downhill. The direction the marbles took as they rolled toward the set-up dominoes was always the same. There was a particular lizard at one end, who crawled up to take the sun in the afternoon. I provoked him, knowing he had a temper since half his tail was missing. As he got angry he turned black with rage and blew a balloon of flesh from his throat—and sat there.

VII

Sitting in the maid's room asking her about her daughter, who is somewhere else. I examine the contents of her dressing table: perfume, comb, hand-mirror, romantic comics, missal.

The maid is sunning rectangles of white cloth on the bushes behind the house. I ask her what they are. She mutters something and moves off. They are bright with whiteness and soft to the touch. I suspect they are a private matter and ask no more about them.

VIII

The river—as I know it—runs from a dam at my cousin's sugar mill down to a pool at the bottom.

On Monday the women make their way to the river, balancing zinc washtubs on a braided cloth on their heads—this cloth has an African name. They take their places at specific rocks and rub, beat, wet, wring, and spread their laundry in the sun. And then leave. The rocks are streaked white after their chore is finished.

This is our land, our river—I have been told. So when women wash their clothes above the place where I swim; when the butcher's wife cleans tripe on Saturday morning; when a group of boys I do not know are using my pool—I hate them for taking up my space.

I hate them for taking up space; I hate them for not including me.

IX

The butcher's wife—after she has cleaned the tripe—comes to wax the parlor floor. She has a daughter my age who today is embarrassed and angry: I think it is because she is wearing one of my old dresses.

(Twenty years later I find she is part of us: "from" my great-uncle.)

There are many mysterious births here.

Three people come up to the steps and ask for my grandfather (who by this time is almost dead). I am suspicious and question them closely. My grandmother explains: "They are your grandfather's outside children."

X

Three women—sisters, my second cousins; unmarried; middle-aged—live across the river. They have a plant called "Midnight Mystery" on their verandah. They come late one night to fetch me and we walk down the path, our way lit by a small boy with a bottle lamp. We balance ourselves across the river and reach the house—in time to see the large white flower unfold.

XI

One reason the parlor floor is waxed on Saturday is that my grandmother holds church on Sunday. People arrive at nine and sit for two hours: giving testimony, singing hymns, reading scripture. They sip South African wine and eat squares of white bread.

Religion looms: Zinc roofs rock on Sunday morning.

XII

The river "comes down": the dam breaks; rocks shift; animals are carried along.

The clouds build across the mountains and move into our valley. Then it rains. Over the rain I can hear the noise of the river. It is a roar; even the gully, which pays the river tribute, roars—and becomes dangerous.

This is clear power.

XIII

We cook on a woodstove in a kitchen behind the house. Our water is taken from the river in brimming kerosene tins. We read by lamp and moon light.

XIV

On one hillside next to the house is the coffee piece: the bushes are low, with dark-green leaves and dark-red fruit. Darkness informs the place. Darkness and damp. Tall trees preserve the dark. Things hide here.

I pick coffee for my grandmother. To be gentle is important: the bushes are sensitive. I carefully fill my basket with the fruit.

XV

After the birth of each of my grandmother's five children the cord was buried and orange trees planted near the house. These trees now bear the names of her children.

XVI

One child died—a son, at eighteen. His grave is in the flower garden, shaded by the orange trees. She tends the grave often, singing "What a Friend We Have in Jesus."

The walls of my grandmother's parlor are decorated with two photographs: of her two remaining sons.

XVII

My mother is my grandmother's daughter. My acquaintance with my mother in this house is from the schoolbooks stored in boxes underneath. Worms have tunneled the pages, the covers are crossed with mold—making the books appear ancient. She has left me to find her here, under this house: I seek identity in a childish hand and obsolete geography.

XVIII

A madwoman steals my grandfather's horse and tries to ride away. I know several madwomen here. She is the boldest; riding bareback, naked. The others walk up and down, talking to themselves and others. One talks to a lizard in the cashew tree at the bottom of the yard. Another sits in the river, refusing to cross.

This woman—one of my cousins—tells me twenty years later about her terror of leaving her place; about the shock treatments the family arranges in town; about how she kept the accounts; about her sister's slow death and how she cared for her.

It must have meant something that all those mad were women. The men were called idiots (an accident of birth)—or drunks.

The women's madness was ascribed to several causes: childlessness, celibacy, "change": such was the nature of their naive science.

XIX

An old woman who sometimes works for us has built a house by the roadside. It is built of clay—from the roadbed—with wood for structure. It has a thatch roof and rests on cement blocks. It is one-room.

She promises to make me a cake if I help her paper the walls. I arrive early, my arms filled with newspapers. We mix flour paste and seek suitable stories for decoration. Pleased with our results, we gather flowers and put them in gourds around the room. True to her word, she bakes me a cake in an empty condensed milk tin.

XX

Walking down to the shop by the railway crossing, saying good morning, people stop me and ask for my mother—often mistaking me for her.

XXI

I want to visit my mother's school where she broke her ankle playing cricket and used the books which now lie under the house. I can't get to the school, but I play cricket; using a carved bamboo root as she did and the dried stalk of a coconut tree for a bat. I play on the same pitch she used—a flat protected place across the road.

XXII

Walking through the water and over the rocks, I am exploring the river—eating bitter susumba and sweet Valencia oranges. Up past pools named for people who drowned there; to the dam; to the sugar mill where I get wet sugar.

XXIII

What is here for me: where do these things lead:

warmth
light
wet sugar
rain and river water
earth
the wood fire
distance
slaughter
mysterious births
fertility
to the women at the river
my grandmother's authority with land and scripture
a tree named with my mother's name.

Twenty years these things rush back at me: the memories of a child inside and outside.

XXIV

Behind the warmth and light are dark and damp/behind the wet sugar, cane fields/behind the rain and river water, periods of drought/underneath the earth are the dead/underneath the wood fire are the ashes to be emptied/underneath the distance is separation/underneath the slaughter is hunger/behind the mysterious births is my own/behind the fertility are the verdicts of insanity/ behind the women at the river are earlier women/underlying my grandmother's authority with land and scripture is obedience to a drunken husband/under a tree named with my mother's name is a rotted cord.

Cliff, a Jamaican-born writer, divides her creative passage into 24 sections that bring to life different elements of her homeland and history. How do the elements of Jamaica she describes here conform to or depart from the way you imagine that country's geography? Does Cliff challenge your assumptions about the island nation? How so?

Collaborate

One of the challenges of creative writing is conveying in words vivid imagery and other sensory details that can capture an audience's imagination. Cliff's "Obsolete Geography" is remarkable for its ability to do this. Using the intense visual power of Cliff's writing as a guide, seek out some photographic images that in some way represent the different sections of her text. (You might consider dividing this task among an entire class or a smaller group.) Once you've found images that match the smaller sections of Cliff's text, show them to the class, explaining why you chose them and how you think they visually represent the style and content of each corresponding section of the text.

Though he died nearly a century ago, naturalist and writer John Muir, according to a Sierra Club biography, is still teaching Americans "the importance of experiencing and protecting our natural heritage. ... His personal and determined involvement in the great conservation questions of the day was and remains an inspiration for environmental activists everywhere." "The American Forests," from which this piece was excerpted, was first published in August 1897 in the Atlantic Monthly.

excerpts from
THE AMERICAN FORESTS

1897

By John Muir

The forests of America, however slighted by man, must have been a great delight to God; for they were the best he ever planted. The whole continent was a garden, and from the beginning it seemed to be favored above all the other wild parks and gardens of the globe. To prepare the ground, it was rolled and sifted in seas with infinite loving deliberation and forethought, lifted into the light, submerged and warmed over and over again, pressed and crumpled into folds and ridges, mountains and hills, subsoiled with heaving volcanic fires, ploughed and ground and sculptured into scenery and soil with glaciers and rivers,—every feature growing and changing from beauty to beauty, higher and higher. And in the fullness of time it was planted in groves, and belts, and broad, exuberant, mantling forests, with the largest, most varied, most fruitful, and most beautiful trees in the world. Bright seas made its border with wave embroidery and icebergs; gray deserts were outspread in the middle of it, mossy tundras on the north, savannas on the south, and blooming prairies and plains; while lakes and rivers shone through all the vast forests and openings, and happy birds and beasts gave delightful animation. Everywhere, everywhere over all the blessed continent, there were beauty, and melody, and kindly, wholesome, foodful abundance.

These forests were composed of about five hundred species of trees, all of them in some way useful to man, ranging in size from twenty-five feet in height and less than one foot in diameter at the ground to four hundred feet in height and more than twenty feet in diameter,—lordly monarchs proclaiming the gospel of beauty like apostles. For many a century after the ice-ploughs were melted, nature fed them and dressed them every day; working like a man, a loving, devoted, painstaking gardener; fingering every leaf and flower and mossy furrowed bole; bending, trimming, modeling, balancing, painting them with the loveliest colors; bringing over them now clouds with cooling shadows and showers, now sunshine; fanning them with gentle winds and rustling their leaves; exercising them in every fibre with storms, and pruning them; loading them with flowers and fruit, loading them with snow, and ever making them more beautiful as the years rolled by. Wide-branching oak and elm in endless variety, walnut and maple, chestnut and beech, ilex and locust, touching limb to limb, spread a leafy translucent canopy along the coast of the Atlantic over the wrinkled folds and ridges of the Alleghanies,—a green billowy sea in summer, golden and purple in autumn, pearly gray like a steadfast frozen mist of interlacing branches and sprays in leafless, restful winter.

To the southward stretched dark, level-topped cypresses in knobby, tangled swamps, grassy savannas in the midst of them like lakes of light, groves of gay sparkling spice-trees, magnolias and palms, glossy-leaved and blooming and shining continually. To the northward, over Maine and the Ottawa, rose hosts of spiry, rosiny evergreens,—white pine and spruce, hemlock and cedar, shoulder to shoulder, laden with purple cones, their myriad needles sparkling and shimmering, covering hills and swamps, rocky headlands and domes, ever bravely aspiring and seeking the sky; the ground in their shade now snow-clad and frozen, now mossy and flowery; beaver meadows here and there, full of lilies and grass; lakes gleaming like eyes, and a silvery embroidery of rivers and creeks watering and brightening all the vast glad wilderness.

Thence westward were oak and elm, hickory and tupelo, gum and liriodendron, sassafras and ash, linden and laurel, spreading on ever wider in glorious exuberance over the great fertile basin of the Mississippi, over damp level bottoms, low dimpling hollows, and round dotting hills, embosoming sunny prairies and cheery park openings, half sunshine, half shade; while a dark wilderness of pines covered the region around the Great Lakes. Thence still westward swept the forests to right and left around grassy plains and deserts a thousand miles wide: irrepressible hosts of spruce and pine, aspen and willow, nut-pine and juniper, cactus and yucca, caring nothing for drought, extending undaunted from mountain to mountain, over mesa and desert, to join the darkening multitudes of pines that covered the high Rocky ranges and the glorious forests along the coast of the moist and balmy Pacific, where new species of pine, giant cedars and spruces, silver firs and sequoias, kings of their race, growing close together like grass in a meadow, poised their brave domes and spires in the sky three hundred feet above the ferns and the lilies that enameled the ground; towering serene through the long centuries, preaching God's forestry fresh from heaven.

Here the forests reached their highest development. Hence they went wavering northward over icy Alaska, brave spruce and fir, poplar and birch, by the coasts and the rivers, to within sight of the Arctic Ocean. American forests! the glory of the world! Surveyed thus from the east to the west, from the north to the south, they are rich beyond thought, immortal, immeasurable, enough and to spare for every feeding, sheltering beast and bird, insect and son of Adam; and nobody need have cared had there been no pines in Norway, no cedars and deodars on Lebanon and the Himalayas, no vine-clad selvas in the basin of the Amazon. With such variety, harmony, and triumphant exuberance, even nature, it would seem, might have rested content with the forests of North America, and planted no more.

So they appeared a few centuries ago when they were rejoicing in wildness. The Indians with stone axes could do them no more harm than could gnawing beavers and browsing moose. Even the fires of the Indians and the fierce shattering lightning seemed to work together only for good in clearing spots here and there for smooth garden prairies, and openings for sunflowers seeking the light. But when the steel axe of the white man rang out in the startled air their doom was sealed. Every tree heard the bodeful sound, and pillars of smoke gave the sign in the sky.

I suppose we need not go mourning the buffaloes. In the nature of things they had to give place to better cattle, though the change might have been made without barbarous wickedness. Likewise many of nature's five hundred kinds of wild trees had to make way for orchards and cornfields. In the settlement and civilization of the country, bread more than timber or beauty was wanted; and in the blindness of hunger, the early settlers, claiming Heaven as their guide, regarded God's trees as only a larger kind of pernicious weeds, extremely hard to get rid of. Accordingly, with no eye to the future, these pious destroyers waged interminable forest wars; chips flew thick and fast; trees in their beauty fell crashing by millions, smashed to confusion, and the smoke of their burning has been rising to heaven more than two hundred years. After the Atlantic coast from Maine to Georgia had been mostly cleared and scorched into melancholy ruins, the overflowing multitude of bread and money seekers poured over the Alleghanies into the fertile middle West, spreading ruthless devastation ever wider and farther over the rich valley of the Mississippi and the vast shadowy pine region about the Great Lakes. Thence still westward the invading horde of destroyers called settlers made its fiery way over the broad Rocky Mountains, felling and burning more fiercely than ever, until at last it has reached the wild side of the continent, and entered the last of the great aboriginal forests on the shores of the Pacific.

Surely, then, it should not be wondered at that lovers of their country, bewailing its baldness, are now crying aloud, "Save what is left of the forests!" Clearing has surely now gone far enough; soon timber will be scarce, and not a grove will be left to rest in or pray in. The remnant protected will yield plenty of timber, a perennial harvest for every right use, without further diminution of its area, and will continue to cover the springs of the rivers that rise in the mountains and give irrigating waters to the dry valleys at their feet, prevent wasting floods and be a blessing to everybody forever. [...]

[...] Emerson says that things refuse to be mismanaged long. An exception would seem to be found in the case of our forests, which have been mismanaged rather long, and now come desperately near being like smashed eggs and spilt milk. Still, in the long run the world does not move backward. The wonderful advance made in the last few years, in creating four national parks in the West, and thirty forest reservations, embracing nearly forty million acres; and in the planting of the borders of streets and highways and spacious parks in all the great cities, to satisfy the natural taste and hunger for landscape beauty and righteousness that God has put, in some measure, into every human being and animal, shows the trend of awakening public opinion. The making of the far-famed New York Central Park was opposed by even good men, with misguided pluck, perseverance, and ingenuity; but straight right won its way, and now that park is appreciated. So we confidently believe it will be with our great national parks and forest reservations. There will be a period of indifference on the part of the rich, sleepy with wealth, and of the toiling millions, sleepy with poverty, most of whom never saw a forest; a period of screaming protest and objection from the plunderers, who are as unconscionable and enterprising as Satan. But light is surely coming, and the friends of destruction will preach and bewail in vain.

The United States government has always been proud of the welcome it has extended to good men of every nation, seeking freedom and homes and bread. Let them be welcomed still as nature welcomes them, to the woods as well as to the prairies and plains. No place is too good for good men, and still there is room. They are invited to heaven, and may well be allowed in America. Every place is made better by them. Let them be as free to pick gold and gems from the hills, to cut and hew, dig and plant, for homes and bread, as the birds are to pick berries from the wild bushes, and moss and leaves for nests. The ground will be glad to feed them, and the pines will come down from the mountains for their homes as willingly as the cedars came from Lebanon for Solomon's temple. Nor will the woods be the worse for this use, or their benign influences be diminished any more than the sun is diminished by shining. Mere destroyers, however, tree-killers, spreading death and confusion in the fairest groves and gardens ever planted, let the government hasten to cast them out and make an end of them. For it must be told again and again, and be burningly borne in mind, that just now, while protective measures are being deliberated languidly, destruction and use are speeding on faster and farther every day. The axe and saw are insanely busy, chips are flying thick as snowflakes, and every summer thousands of acres of priceless forests, with their underbrush, soil, springs, climate, scenery, and religion, are vanishing away in clouds of smoke, while, except in the national parks, not one forest guard is employed.

All sorts of local laws and regulations have been tried and found wanting, and the costly lessons of our own experience, as well as that of every civilized nation, show conclusively that the fate of the remnant of our forests is in the hands of the federal government, and that if the remnant is to be saved at all, it must be saved quickly.

Any fool can destroy trees. They cannot run away; and if they could, they would still be destroyed,—chased and hunted down as long as fun or a dollar could be got out of their bark hides, branching horns, or magnificent bole backbones. Few that fell trees plant them; nor would planting avail much towards getting back anything like the noble primeval forests. During a man's life only saplings can be grown, in the place of the old trees—tens of centuries old—that have been destroyed. It took more than three thousand years to make some of the trees in these Western woods,—trees that are still standing in perfect strength and beauty, waving and singing in the mighty forests of the Sierra. Through all the wonderful, eventful centuries since Christ's time—and long before that—

God has cared for these trees, saved them from drought, disease, avalanches, and a thousand straining, leveling tempests and floods; but he cannot save them from fools,—only Uncle Sam can do that.

Muir's "The American Forests" was originally published in 1897, but its message—that we need to better manage our natural resources—does not seem so dated. Using your library's databases, try to find a modern editorial or letter to the editor that shares a message similar to Muir's. What similarities do you notice? Why do you think this message stands the test of time?

Muir's piece is remarkable in its use of highly descriptive language. Why do you think he makes such an effort to vividly describe the forests? How does this language help him persuade readers of his claim?

Think about the forests, mountains, swamps, beaches, valleys, or lakes (among other possible natural landscapes) that make up your local surroundings. With one of these sites in mind, write a short passage in which you imitate Muir's descriptive prose.

Author and journalist Bruce Watson, whose work has appeared in many national publications, wrote this appreciation for Rachel Carson and her historic book Silent Spring *for* Smithsonian Magazine *in September 2002. An excerpt from* Silent Spring *follows "Sounding the Alarm."*

SOUNDING THE ALARM

By Bruce Watson

A month before World War II ended, a relatively unknown writer named Rachel Carson proposed an article for *Reader's Digest* about the effects of the pesticide DDT on what she called "the delicate balance of nature." The shy woman assured the editors that "it's something that really does affect everybody." They turned her down. Perhaps they felt a story about pesticides would be too depressing. Or maybe it was that DDT, then widely used in the United States, had likely saved thousands of American Marines and soldiers by killing disease-carrying insects on far-off beachheads. Carson filed the subject away and went on to write best-selling books on the wonders of the sea. A dozen years later, she decided to take up the topic again. This time would be different.

While authors and publishers like to believe that a single book can change the world, few books actually have had such an impact. Yet the day it hit bookstores more than 40 years ago, Rachel Carson's *Silent Spring* fueled a vigorous public debate about the use of chemicals in our environment that has yet to be resolved. "Without this book," wrote former Vice President Al Gore in the introduction to a 1994 reprint of it, "the environmental movement might have been long delayed or never have developed at all." This complex, lyrical volume led not only to the banning of DDT but eventually to the formation of the U.S. Environmental Protection Agency. "After *Silent Spring*, people began to think about the chemicals they were handling, what they were doing to the environment, and what scientists weren't telling them," says Carson biographer Linda Lear (*Rachel Carson: Witness for Nature*, 1997). "They began to question the very direction of technology."

Carson had no intention of starting a movement. Working against time following a diagnosis of cancer, she sounded her wake-up call in the name of songbirds. "If I kept silent I could never again listen to a thrush's song without overwhelming self-reproach," she wrote. But in the fall of 1962, many scientists and people in the chemical industry wished she had kept silent.

Growing up in western Pennsylvania, Rachel Louise Carson, known to friends as Ray, immersed herself in nature and books, especially the sea sagas of Melville and Conrad. At the Pennsylvania College for Women in the mid-1920s she changed her major from English to Biology, but retained a deep love of writing. Eventually she earned a master's degree in Marine Zoology from Johns Hopkins University and became a junior aquatic biologist for the U.S. Bureau of Fisheries in Washington, D.C. Her first book, *Under the Sea-Wind*, was published in 1941 and sold fewer than 2,000 copies. But it put her in contact with scientists who were beginning to ask hard questions about the fate of the Earth.

In the late 1940s, while working as publications editor for the Fish and Wildlife Service, she began her second book, *The Sea Around Us*. The literary sensation of 1951—topping best-seller lists and winning a National Book Award—it outlined the latest science informing our understanding of the ocean. Carson almost instantly became the nation's unofficial spokesperson for the sea. "Heavens!" she wrote a friend after winning another accolade. "Is this all about me—it is really ridiculous!" *Sea's* success enabled her to become a full-time writer and buy a cottage on the coast of Maine, which would become a sanctuary for the rest of her life. While she would write another book about the sea, she continued to harbor nagging questions about the effect of pesticides on the land.

Dichlorodiphenyltrichloroethane (DDT) was first used as an insecticide in 1939. Just a few grains of the white powder would miraculously wipe out colonies of mosquito larvae. During World War II, B-25 bombers sprayed DDT prior to invasions in the Pacific. After the war, DDT would all but wipe out malaria in the developed world and drastically reduce it elsewhere. (The National Academy of Sciences reported in 1970 that DDT had saved more than 500 million lives from malaria.) Paul Muller, the chemist who first turned it on unsuspecting flies, won a Nobel Prize in 1948 for his work.

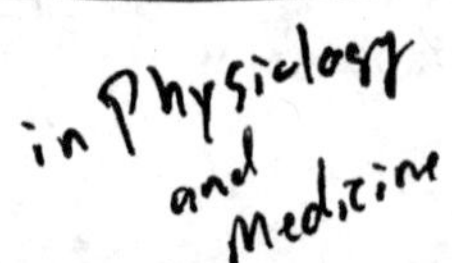

By the late 1950s, DDT production had nearly quintupled from World War II levels as municipal authorities took to spraying the chemical on American suburbs to eradicate tent caterpillars, gypsy moths and the beetles that carried Dutch elm disease.

But the chemical had a disturbing characteristic: it killed indiscriminately. After finding seven dead songbirds in her yard after the area had been sprayed against mosquitoes, a Massachusetts friend of Carson's wrote a letter to the *Boston Herald* in 1958 demanding that officials "stop the spraying of poisons from the air." Carson read the letter and realized that "everything which meant most to me as a naturalist was being threatened." She decided to make DDT the subject of her next book, tentatively entitled *Man Against the Earth.*

But working on it in 1960, she was diagnosed with breast cancer and underwent a mastectomy. Subsequent radiation treatments left her nauseated and bedridden. The book she had expected to finish in a few months dragged on for four years. Finally, in June 1962, the first of a three-part excerpt from *Silent Spring* appeared in the *New Yorker* magazine.

Before the final installment hit newsstands, the Velsicol Corporation, which manufactured the pesticide chlordane (banned in 1988), threatened to sue the magazine for libel. "Everything in those articles has been checked and is true," replied the *New Yorker's* legal counsel. "Go ahead and sue." The company never did, but the attacks had only begun. One reader wrote that Carson's work "probably reflects her Communist sympathies."

Then, in July, news broke that a supposedly harmless drug given to thousands of pregnant women in Europe for morning sickness had been determined to cause widespread birth defects. Newspapers and magazines ran photographs of babies born without arms and legs or otherwise physically deformed. "It's all of a piece," said Carson. "Thalidomide and pesticides—they represent our willingness to rush ahead and use something new without knowing what the results are going to be."

Suddenly in a single summer, chemical science had fallen from its pedestal. By late August, reporters were asking President Kennedy if federal officials would be investigating the long-range effects of pesticides. "They already are," he answered. "I think particularly, of course, since Miss Carson's book, but they are examining the matter."

Silent Spring went on sale September 27 and raced to the top of the *New York Times* best-seller list where it stayed for most of the fall. By Christmas, the book, which begins with Carson's fable about an idyllic countryside that teemed with wildlife until "a strange blight crept over the area and everything began to change," had sold more than 100,000 copies. In subsequent chapters, the author followed the trail of pesticides from farm to family table, provided a "Who's Who" of toxic chemicals—DDT, chlordane, malathion, parathion—and noted that pesticides accumulate in fatty tissues of organisms.

Reaction to *Silent Spring* was quick, strong and largely negative. *Life* claimed that Carson had "overstated her case." *Time*, citing scientists' claims that insecticides were "harmless," dismissed it as an "emotional and inaccurate outburst." The chemical and food industries came after Carson aggressively. *Chemical and Engineering News*, a chemical industry trade magazine, linked Carson with "pseudo-scientists and faddists," denounced her "high-pitched sequences of anxieties," and belittled her credentials. The Nutrition Foundation mailed scathing reviews of the book to newspapers. The National Agricultural Chemicals Association launched a $250,000 campaign to refute it, and the Monsanto Corporation published a parody of Carson's opening fable, describing a world without pesticides, overrun by insects and disease. In a cartoon in the November 10, 1962, issue of the *Saturday Review*, a man lamented "I had just come to terms with fallout, and along comes Rachel Carson."

But there were voices of praise as well. Supreme Court Justice William O. Douglas called *Silent Spring* "the most important chronicle of this century for the human race."

While undergoing debilitating radiation treatments, Carson answered her critics.

No civilization, she said, "can wage relentless war on life without destroying itself, and without losing the right to be called civilized." She insisted she was not against all pesticides and had never called for banning them, only for restricting their use. Public opinion wavered. Then television tipped the scales in her favor.

In April 1963, 15 million Americans watched *CBS Reports*' "The Silent Spring of Rachel Carson." "We still talk in terms of conquest," Carson said. "I think we're challenged, as mankind has never been challenged before, to prove our maturity and our mastery, not of nature but of ourselves." Her thoughtful and reserved presentation struck a chord with viewers: hundreds wrote concerned letters to

Carson, CBS, the USDA, the Public Health Service, and the FDA. A month later, President Kennedy's Science Advisory Committee released its own report on pesticides, which backed Carson's thesis, criticized the government and the chemical industry, and called for "orderly reductions of persistent pesticides."

Today, despite the banning of DDT in 1972, pesticides are still widely used, and Carson, who died in 1964 at age 56 of heart disease and the cancer she battled so valiantly, still comes in for criticism. "Rachel Carson's book was a brilliant piece of writing and a seminal work, but it's clear now that she was more fearful of pesticides than was warranted," says Dennis Avery, former senior agriculture expert with the State Department and author of Saving the Planet With Pesticides and Plastic. While admitting that some dangers exist to the farmers who handle concentrated amounts of pesticides, Avery maintains that the "Green Revolution" of fertilizers, pesticides and genetically improved seeds has tripled crop yields since 1950 and saved 12 million square miles of natural habitat that otherwise would have been cleared for farmland in order to maintain the nation's food supply.

But veteran environmentalist Barry Commoner insists that pesticides remain a significant danger to the environment and human health. "Enough is known now that we could greatly reduce and eventually eliminate the harm caused by our use of pesticides and herbicides through organic farming and integrated pest management," he says. "We are still exposed to pesticides in our diet, and not much is known about their medical consequences. Since *Silent Spring*, the only real improvement has been for the birds. Thanks to the elimination of DDT, the osprey are better off, but I don't think we are."

Silent Spring reported that chemical companies in the United States produced about 32,000 tons of pesticides in 1960. Today the EPA says that farmers, consumers and the government use about 615,000 tons of conventional pesticides each year. (Most pesticides used today, however, are less toxic and break down faster in nature than those used 40 years ago.) And, as Carson warned, insects continue to develop chemical resistance. According to the Worldwatch Institute, an environmental policy think tank, a higher percentage of crops in America are now lost to pests than before pesticides were first widely used. In an attempt to safeguard Americans' food, Congress passed the Food Quality Protection Act in 1996, giving the EPA a decade to re-evaluate the safety of 9,000 pesticides.

If debate over Carson's thesis continues, few doubt her impact. "Rachel Carson's legacy has less to do with pesticides than with awakening of environmental consciousness," says biographer Lear. "She changed the way we look at nature. We now know that we are a part of nature, and we can't damage it without it coming back to bite us."

Rachel Carson's 1962 book Silent Spring, *from which this piece is excerpted, is one of the most influential works in American history. For more information about Carson and her book, see Bruce Watson's essay "Sounding the Alarm," which precedes this one.*

THE OBLIGATION TO ENDURE

By Rachel Carson

The history of life on earth has been a history of interaction between living things and their surroundings. To a large extent, the physical form and the habits of the earth's vegetation and its animal life have been molded by the environment. Considering the whole span of earthly time, the opposite effect, in which life actually modifies its surroundings, has been relatively slight. Only within the moment of time represented by the present century has one species—man—acquired significant power to alter the nature of his world.

During the past quarter century this power has not only increased to one of disturbing magnitude but it has changed in character. The most alarming of all man's assaults upon the environment is the contamination of air, earth, rivers, and sea with dangerous and even lethal materials. This pollution is for the most part irrecoverable; the chain of evil it initiates not only in the world that must support life but in living tissues is for the most part irreversible. In this now universal contamination of the environment, chemicals are the sinister and little recognized partners of radiation in changing the very nature of the world—the very nature of its life. Strontium 90, released through nuclear explosions into the air, comes to earth in rain or drifts down as fallout, lodges in soil, enters into the grass or corn or wheat grown there, and in time takes up its abode in the bones of a human being, there to remain until his death. Similarly, chemicals sprayed on croplands or forests or gardens lie long in soil, entering into living organisms, passing from one to another in a chain of poisoning and death. Or they pass mysteriously by underground streams until they emerge and, through the alchemy of air and sunlight, combine into new forms, that kill vegetation, sicken cattle, and work unknown harm on those who drink from once pure wells. As Albert Schweitzer has said, "Man can hardly even recognize the devils of his own creation."

It took hundreds of millions of years to produce the life that now inhabits the earth—eons of time in which that developing and evolving and diversifying life reached a state of adjustment and balance with its surroundings. The environment, rigorously shaping and directing the life it supports, contained elements that were hostile as well as supporting. Certain rocks gave out dangerous radiation; even within the light of the sun, from which all life draws its energy, there were short-wave radiations with power to injure. Given time—not in years but in millennia—life adjusts, and a balance has been reached. For time is the essential ingredient; but in the modern world there is no time.

The rapidity of change and the speed with which new situations are created follow the impetuous and heedless pace of man rather than the deliberate pace of nature. Radiation is no longer merely the background radiation of rocks, the bombardment of cosmic rays, the ultraviolet of the sun that have existed before there was any life on earth; radiation is now the unnatural creation of man's tampering with the atom. The chemicals to which life is asked to make its adjustment are no longer merely the calcium and silica and copper and all the rest of the minerals washed out of the rocks and carried in rivers to the sea; they are the synthetic creations of man's inventive mind, brewed in his laboratories, and having no counterparts in nature.

To adjust to these chemicals would require time on the scale that is nature's; it would require not merely the years of a man's life but the life of generations. And even this, were it by some miracle possible, would be futile, for the new chemicals come from our laboratories in an endless stream; almost five hundred annually find their way into actual use in the United States alone. The figure is staggering and its implications are not easily grasped—500 new chemicals to which the bodies of men and animals are required somehow to adapt each year, chemicals totally outside the limits of biologic experience.

Among them are many that are used in man's war against nature. Since the mid-1940's over 200 basic chemicals have been created for use in killing insects, weeds, rodents, and other organisms described in the modern vernacular as "pests"; and they are sold under several thousand different brand names.

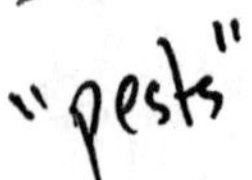

These sprays, dusts, and aerosols are now applied almost universally to farms, gardens, forests, and homes—nonselective chemicals that have the power to kill every insect, the "good" and the "bad," to still the song of birds and the leaping of fish in the streams, to coat the leaves with a deadly film, and to linger on in soil—all this though the intended target may be only a few weeds or insects. Can anyone believe it is possible to lay down such a barrage of poisons on the surface of the earth without making it unfit for all life? They should not be called "insecticides," but "biocides."

The whole process of spraying seems caught up in an endless spiral. Since DDT was released for civilian use, a process of escalation has been going on in which ever more toxic materials must be found. This has happened because insects, in a triumphant vindication of Darwin's principle of the survival of the fittest, have evolved super races immune to the particular insecticide used, hence a deadlier one has always to be developed and then a deadlier one than that. It has happened also because, for reasons to be described later, destructive insects often undergo a "flareback," or resurgence, after spraying, in numbers greater than before. Thus the chemical war is never won, and all life is caught in its violent crossfire.

Along with the possibility of the extinction of mankind by nuclear war, the central problem of our age has therefore become the contamination of man's total environment with such substances of incredible potential for harm—substances that accumulate in the tissues of plants and animals and even penetrate the germ cells to shatter or alter the very material of heredity upon which the shape of the future depends.

Some would-be architects of our future look toward a time when it will be possible to alter the human germ plasm by design. But we may easily be doing so now by inadvertence, for many chemicals, like radiation, bring about gene mutations. It is ironic to think that man might determine his own future by something so seemingly trivial as the choice of an insect spray.

All this has been risked—for what? Future historians may well be amazed by our distorted sense of proportion. How could intelligent beings seek to control a few unwanted species by a method that contaminated the entire environment and brought the threat of disease and death even to their own kind?

Yet this is precisely what we have done. We have done it, moreover, for reasons that collapse the moment we examine them. We are told that the enormous and expanding use of pesticides is necessary to maintain farm production. Yet is our real problem not one of *overproduction*? Our farms, despite measures to remove acreages from production and to pay farmers *not* to produce, have yielded such a staggering excess of crops that the American taxpayer in 1962 is paying out more than one billion dollars a year as the total carrying cost of the surplus-food storage program. And is the situation helped when one branch of the Agriculture Department tries to reduce production while another states, as it did in 1958, "It is believed generally that reduction of crop acreages under provisions of the Soil Bank will stimulate interest in use of chemicals to obtain maximum production on the land retained in crops."

All this is not to say there is no insect problem and no need of control. I am saying, rather, that control must be geared to realities, not to mythical situations, and that the methods employed must be such that they do not destroy us along with the insects.

The problem whose attempted solution has brought such a train of disaster in its wake is an accompaniment of our modern way of life. Long before the age of man, insects inhabited the earth—a group of extraordinarily varied and adaptable beings. Over the course of time since man's advent, a small percentage of the more than half a million species of insects have come into conflict with human welfare in two principal ways: as competitors for the food supply and as carriers of human disease.

Disease-carrying insects become important where human beings are crowded together, especially under conditions where sanitation is poor, as in time of natural disaster or war or in situations of extreme poverty and deprivation. Then control of some sort becomes necessary. It is a sobering fact, however, as we shall presently see, that the method of massive chemical control has had only limited success, and also threatens to worsen the very conditions it is intended to curb.

Under primitive agricultural conditions the farmer had few insect problems. These arose with the intensification of agriculture—the devotion of immense acreages to a single crop. Such a system set the stage for explosive increases in specific insect populations. Single-crop farming does not take advantage of the principles by which nature works; it is agriculture as an engineer might conceive it to be. Nature has introduced great variety into the landscape, but man has displayed a passion for simplifying it. Thus he undoes the built-in checks and balances by which nature holds the species within bounds. One important natural check is a limit on the amount of suitable habitat for each species. Obviously then, an insect that lives on wheat can build up its population to much higher levels on a farm devoted to wheat than on one in which wheat is intermingled with other crops to which the insect is not adapted.

The same thing happens in other situations. A generation or more ago, the towns of large areas of the United States lined their streets with the noble elm tree. Now the beauty they hopefully created is threatened with complete destruction as disease sweeps through the elms, carried by a beetle that would have only limited chance to build up large populations and to spread from tree to tree if the elms were only occasional trees in a richly diversified planting.

Another factor in the modern insect problem is one that must be viewed against a background of geologic and human history: the spreading of thousands of different kinds of organisms from their native homes to invade new territories. This worldwide migration has been studied and graphically described by the British ecologist Charles Elton in his recent book *The Ecology of Invasions.* During the Cretaceous Period, some hundred million years ago, flooding seas cut many land bridges between continents and living things found themselves confined in what Elton calls "colossal separate nature reserves." There, isolated from others of their kind, they developed many new species. When some of the land masses were joined again, about 15 million years ago, these species began to move out into new territories—a movement that is not only still in progress but is now receiving considerable assistance from man.

The importation of plants is the primary agent in the modern spread of species, for animals have almost invariably gone along with the plants, quarantine being a comparatively recent and not completely effective innovation. The United States Office of Plant Introduction alone has introduced almost 200,000 species and varieties of plants from all over the world. Nearly half of the 180 or so major insect enemies of plants in the United States are accidental imports from abroad, and most of them have come as hitchhikers on plants.

In new territory, out of reach of the restraining hand of the natural enemies that kept down its numbers in its native land, an invading plant or animal is able to become enormously abundant. Thus it is no accident that our most troublesome insects are introduced species.

These invasions, both the naturally occurring and those dependent on human assistance, are likely to continue indefinitely. Quarantine and massive chemical campaigns are only extremely expensive ways of buying time. We are faced, according to Dr. Elton, "with a life-and-death need not just to find new technological means of suppressing this plant or that animal"; instead we need the basic knowledge of animal populations and their relations to their surroundings that will "promote an even balance and damp down the explosive power of outbreaks and new invasions." Much of the necessary knowledge is now available but we do not use it. We train ecologists in our universities and even employ them in our governmental agencies but we seldom take their advice. We allow the chemical death rain to fall as though there were no alternative, whereas in fact there are many, and our ingenuity could soon discover many more if given opportunity.

Have we fallen into a mesmerized state that makes us accept as inevitable that which is inferior or detrimental, as though having lost the will or the vision to demand that which is good? Such thinking, in the words of the ecologist Paul Shepard, "idealizes life with only its head out of water, inches above the limits of toleration of the corruption of its own environment ... Why should we tolerate a diet of weak poisons, a home in insipid surroundings, a circle of acquaintances who are not quite our enemies, the noise of motors with just enough relief to prevent insanity? Who would want to live in a world which is just not quite fatal?"

Yet such a world is pressed upon us. The crusade to create a chemically sterile, insect-free world seems to have engendered a fanatic zeal on the part of many specialists and most of the so-called control agencies. On every hand there is evidence that those engaged in spraying operations exercise a ruthless power. "The regulatory entomologists ... function as prosecutor, judge and jury, tax assessor and collector and sheriff to enforce their own orders," said Connecticut entomologist Neely Turner. The most flagrant abuses go unchecked in both state and federal agencies.

It is not my contention that chemical insecticides must never be used. I do contend that we have put poisonous and biologically potent chemicals indiscriminately into the hands of persons largely or wholly ignorant of their potentials for harm. We have subjected enormous numbers of people to contact with these poisons, without their consent and often without their knowledge. If the Bill of Rights contains no guarantee that a citizen shall be secure against lethal poisons appeal

distributed either by private individuals or by public officials, it is surely only because our forefathers, despite their considerable wisdom and foresight, could conceive of no such problem.

I contend, furthermore, that we have allowed these chemicals to be used with little or no advance investigation of their effect on soil, water, wildlife, and man himself. Future generations are unlikely to condone our lack of prudent concern for the integrity of the natural world that supports all life.

There is still very limited awareness of the nature of the threat. This is an era of specialists, each of whom sees his own problem and is unaware of or intolerant of the larger frame into which it fits. It is also an era dominated by industry, in which the right to make a dollar at whatever cost is seldom challenged. When the public protests, confronted with some obvious evidence of damaging results of pesticide applications, it is fed little tranquilizing pills of half truth. We urgently need an end to these false assurances, to the sugar coating of unpalatable facts. It is the public that is being asked to assume the risks that the insect controllers calculate. The public must decide whether it wishes to continue on the present road, and it can do so only when in full possession of the facts. In the words of Jean Rostand, "The obligation to endure gives us the right to know."

Explore

As Bruce Watson explains, Carson won over the American public in the face of harsh criticism of *Silent Spring* with a reasoned defense of her work and her purpose. Find video, audio, and/or written texts online that discuss Carson, her work, and reaction to *Silent Spring*, and discuss the rhetorical appeals used to defend the nascent environmental movement to which Carson contributed.

Collaborate

Silent Spring played a crucial role in setting off the environmental movement, leading to the ban of DDT and to the formation of the EPA. Carson's ideas about how to protect the environment have survived as well. As part of a group, read the following texts in this book and discuss how Carson's ideas emerge within them. In some cases these pieces echo and develop Carson's ideas, and in others they challenge her claims or otherwise transform them. Characterize the links and identify the passages in *Silent Spring* that help you make these connections.

Marvin Gaye's "Mercy Mercy Me" (page 6)

Stewart Brand's "Reframing the Problems" (page 167)

Naomi Klein's "A Hole in the World" (page 65)

Compose

Write short passage in which you summarize Carson's claim and supporting reasons. Given the purpose of her piece, how do you think she appeals to her readers? What do you find especially persuasive and why?

Award-winning journalist and author Naomi Klein wrote this article for the London-based newspaper The Guardian *in June 2010. In its introduction to the piece, the newspaper wrote: "The Deepwater Horizon disaster is not just an industrial accident—it is a violent wound inflicted on the Earth itself. In this special report from the Gulf coast, a leading author and activist shows how it lays bare the hubris at the heart of capitalism."*

A HOLE IN THE WORLD

BY NAOMI KLEIN

Everyone gathered for the town hall meeting had been repeatedly instructed to show civility to the gentlemen from BP and the federal government. These fine folks had made time in their busy schedules to come to a high school gymnasium on a Tuesday night in Plaquemines Parish, Louisiana, one of many coastal communities where brown poison was slithering through the marshes, part of what has come to be described as the largest environmental disaster in U.S. history.

"Speak to others the way you would want to be spoken to," the chair of the meeting pleaded one last time before opening the floor for questions.

And for a while the crowd, mostly made up of fishing families, showed remarkable restraint. They listened patiently to Larry Thomas, a genial BP public relations flack, as he told them that he was committed to "doing better" to process their claims for lost revenue—then passed all the details off to a markedly less friendly subcontractor. They heard out the suit from the Environmental Protection Agency as he informed them that, contrary to what they have read about the lack of testing and the product being banned in Britain, the chemical dispersant being sprayed on the oil in massive quantities was really perfectly safe.

But patience started running out by the third time Ed Stanton, a coast guard captain, took to the podium to reassure them that "the coast guard intends to make sure that BP cleans it up."

The Deepwater Horizon

"Put it in writing!" someone shouted out. By now, the air conditioning had shut itself off and the coolers of Budweiser were running low. A shrimper named Matt O'Brien approached the mic. "We don't need to hear this anymore," he declared, hands on hips. It didn't matter what assurances they were offered because, he explained, "we just don't trust you guys!" And with that, such a loud cheer rose up from the floor you'd have thought the Oilers (the unfortunately named school football team) had scored a touchdown.

The showdown was cathartic, if nothing else. For weeks residents had been subjected to a barrage of pep talks and extravagant promises coming from Washington, Houston and London. Every time they turned on their TVs, there was the BP boss, Tony Hayward, offering his solemn word that he would "make it right." Or else it was President Barack Obama expressing his absolute confidence that his administration would "leave the Gulf coast in better shape than it was before," that he was "making sure" it "comes back even stronger than it was before this crisis."

It all sounded great. But for people whose livelihoods put them in intimate contact with the delicate chemistry of the wetlands, it also sounded completely ridiculous, painfully so. Once the oil coats the base of the marsh grass, as it had already done just a few miles from here, no miracle machine or chemical concoction could safely get it out. You can skim oil off the surface of open water, and you can rake it off a sandy beach, but an oiled marsh just sits there, slowly dying. The larvae of countless species for which the marsh is a spawning ground—shrimp, crab, oysters and fin fish—will be poisoned.

It was already happening. Earlier that day, I travelled through nearby marshes in a shallow water boat. Fish were jumping in waters encircled by white boom, the strips of thick cotton and mesh BP is using to soak up the oil. The circle of fouled material seemed to be tightening around the fish like a noose. Nearby, a red-winged blackbird perched atop a 2-metre (7-foot) blade of oil-contaminated marsh grass. Death was creeping up the cane; the small bird may as well have been standing on a lit stick of dynamite.

And then there is the grass itself, or the Roseau cane, as the tall sharp blades are called. If oil seeps deeply enough into the marsh, it will not only kill the grass above ground but also the roots. Those roots are what hold the marsh together, keeping bright green land from collapsing into the Mississippi River delta and the Gulf of Mexico. So not only do places like Plaquemines Parish stand to lose their fisheries, but also much of the physical barrier that lessens the intensity of fierce storms like Hurricane Katrina. Which could mean losing everything.

How long will it take for an ecosystem this ravaged to be "restored and made whole" as Obama's interior secretary has pledged to do? It's not at all clear that such a thing is remotely possible, at least not in a time frame we can easily wrap our heads around. The Alaskan fisheries have yet to fully recover from the 1989 Exxon Valdez spill and some species of fish never returned. Government scientists now estimate that as much as a Valdez-worth of oil may be entering the Gulf coastal waters every four days. An even worse prognosis emerges from the 1991 Gulf war spill, when an estimated 11 million barrels of oil were dumped into the Persian Gulf—the largest spill ever. That oil entered the marshland and stayed there, burrowing deeper and deeper thanks to holes dug by crabs. It's not a perfect comparison, since so little clean-up was done, but according to a study conducted 12 years after the disaster, nearly 90% of the impacted muddy salt marshes and mangroves were still profoundly damaged.

We do know this. Far from being "made whole," the Gulf coast, more than likely, will be diminished. Its rich waters and crowded skies will be less alive than they are today. The physical space many communities occupy on the map will also shrink, thanks to erosion. And the coast's legendary culture will contract and wither. The fishing families up and down the coast do not just gather food, after all. They hold up an intricate network that includes family tradition, cuisine, music, art and endangered languages—much like the roots of grass holding up the land in the marsh. Without fishing, these unique cultures lose their root system, the very ground on which they stand. (BP, for its part, is well aware of the limits of recovery. The company's Gulf of Mexico regional oil spill response plan specifically instructs officials not to make "promises that property, ecology, or anything else will be restored to normal." Which is no doubt why its officials consistently favour folksy terms like "make it right.")

If Katrina pulled back the curtain on the reality of racism in America, the BP disaster pulls back the curtain on something far more hidden: how little control even the most ingenious among us have over the awesome, intricately interconnected natural forces with which we so casually meddle. BP cannot plug the hole in the Earth that it made. Obama cannot order fish species to survive, or brown pelicans not to go extinct (no matter whose ass he kicks). No amount of money—not BP's recently pledged $20 billion (£13.5 billion), not $100 billion—can replace a culture that has lost its roots. And while our politicians and corporate leaders have yet to come to terms with these humbling truths, the people whose air, water and livelihoods have been contaminated are losing their illusions fast.

"Everything is dying," a woman said as the town hall meeting was finally coming to a close. "How can you honestly tell us that our Gulf is resilient and will bounce back? Because not one of you up here has a hint as to what is going to happen to our Gulf. You sit up here with a straight face and act like you know when you don't know."

This Gulf coast crisis is about many things—corruption, deregulation, the addiction to fossil fuels. But underneath it all, it's about this: our culture's excruciatingly dangerous claim to have such complete understanding and command over nature that we can radically manipulate and re-engineer it with minimal risk to the natural systems that sustain us. But as the BP disaster has revealed, nature is always more unpredictable than the most sophisticated mathematical and geological models imagine. During Thursday's congressional testimony, Hayward said: "The best minds and the deepest expertise are being brought to bear" on the crisis, and that, "with the possible exception of the space programme in the 1960s, it is difficult to imagine the gathering of a larger, more technically proficient team in one place in peacetime." And yet, in the face of what the geologist Jill Schneiderman has described as "Pandora's well," they are like the men at the front of that gymnasium: they act like they know, but they don't know.

BP'S MISSION STATEMENT

In the arc of human history, the notion that nature is a machine for us to re-engineer at will is a relatively recent conceit. In her ground-breaking 1980 book *The Death of Nature*, the environmental historian Carolyn Merchant reminded readers that up until the 1600s, the Earth was alive, usually taking the form of a mother. Europeans—like indigenous people the world over—believed the planet to be a living organism, full of life-giving powers but also wrathful tempers. There were, for this reason, strong taboos against actions that would deform and desecrate "the mother," including mining.

The metaphor changed with the unlocking of some (but by no means all) of nature's mysteries during the scientific revolution of the 1600s. With nature now cast as a machine, devoid of mystery or divinity, its component parts could be dammed, extracted and remade with impunity. Nature still sometimes appeared as a woman, but one easily dominated and subdued. Sir Francis Bacon best encapsulated the new ethos when he wrote in the 1623 "De dignitate et augmentis scientiarum" that nature is to be "put in constraint, moulded, and made as it were new by art and the hand of man."

Those words may as well have been BP's corporate mission statement. Boldly inhabiting what the company called "the energy frontier," it dabbled in synthesising methane-producing microbes and announced that "a new area of investigation" would be geoengineering. And of course it bragged that, at its Tiber prospect in the Gulf of Mexico, it now had "the deepest well ever drilled by the oil and gas industry"—as deep under the ocean floor as jets fly overhead.

Imagining and preparing for what would happen if these experiments in altering the building blocks of life and geology went wrong occupied precious little space in the corporate imagination. As we have all discovered, after the Deepwater Horizon rig exploded on 20 April, the company had no systems in place to effectively respond to this scenario. Explaining why it did not have even the ultimately unsuccessful containment dome waiting to be activated on shore, a BP spokesman, Steve Rinehart, said: "I don't think anybody foresaw the circumstance that we're faced with now." Apparently, it "seemed inconceivable" that the blowout preventer would ever fail—so why prepare?

This refusal to contemplate failure clearly came straight from the top. A year ago, Hayward told a group of graduate students at Stanford University that he has a plaque on his desk that reads: "If you knew you could not fail, what would you try?" Far from being a benign inspirational slogan, this was actually an accurate description of how BP and its competitors behaved in the real world. In recent hearings on Capitol Hill, congressman Ed Markey of Massachusetts grilled representatives from the top oil and gas companies on the revealing ways in which they had allocated resources. Over three years, they had spent "$39 billion to explore for new oil and gas. Yet, the average investment in research and development for safety, accident prevention and spill response was a paltry $20 million a year."

These priorities go a long way towards explaining why the initial exploration plan that BP submitted to the federal government for the ill-fated Deepwater Horizon well reads like a Greek tragedy about human hubris. The phrase "little risk" appears five times. Even if there is a spill, BP confidently predicts that, thanks to "proven equipment and technology," adverse affects will be minimal. Presenting nature as a predictable and agreeable junior partner (or perhaps subcontractor), the report cheerfully explains that should a spill occur, "Currents and microbial degradation would remove the oil from the water column or dilute the constituents to background levels." The effects on fish, meanwhile, "would likely be sublethal" because of "the capability of adult fish and shellfish to avoid a spill [and] to metabolise hydrocarbons". (In BP's telling, rather than a dire threat, a spill emerges as an all-you-can-eat buffet for aquatic life.)

Best of all, should a major spill occur, there is, apparently, "little risk of contact or impact to the coastline" because of the company's projected speedy response (!) and "due to the distance [of the rig] to shore"—about 48 miles (77 kilometres). This is the most astonishing claim of all. In a gulf that often sees winds of more than 70 kilometres an hour, not to mention hurricanes, BP had so little respect for the ocean's capacity to ebb and flow, surge and heave, that it did not think oil could make a paltry 77 kilometre trip. (Last week, a shard of the exploded Deepwater Horizon showed up on a beach in Florida, 306 kilometres away.)

None of this sloppiness would have been possible, however, had BP not been making its predictions to a political class eager to believe that nature had indeed been mastered. Some, like Republican Lisa Murkowski, were more eager than others. The Alaskan senator was so awe-struck by the industry's four-dimensional seismic imaging that she proclaimed deep-sea drilling to have reached the very height of controlled artificiality. "It's better than Disneyland in terms of how you can take technologies and go after a resource that is thousands of years old and do so in an environmentally sound way," she told the Senate energy committee just seven months ago.

Drilling without thinking has of course been Republican party policy since May 2008. With gas prices soaring to unprecedented heights, that's when the conservative leader Newt Gingrich unveiled the slogan "Drill Here, Drill Now, Pay Less"—with an emphasis on the now. The wildly popular campaign was a cry against caution, against study, against measured action. In Gingrich's telling, drilling at home wherever the oil and gas might be—locked in Rocky Mountain shale, in the Arctic National Wildlife Refuge, and deep offshore—was a surefire way to lower the price at the pump, create jobs, and kick Arab ass all at once. In the face of this triple win, caring about the environment was for sissies: as senator Mitch McConnell put it, "in Alabama and Mississippi and Louisiana and Texas, they think oil rigs are pretty." By the time the infamous "Drill Baby Drill" Republican national convention rolled around, the party base was in such a frenzy for U.S.-made fossil fuels, they would have bored under the convention floor if someone had brought a big enough drill.

Obama, eventually, gave in, as he invariably does. With cosmic bad timing, just three weeks before the Deepwater Horizon blew up, the president announced he would open up previously protected parts of the country to offshore drilling. The practice was not as risky as he had thought, he explained. "Oil rigs today generally don't cause spills. They are technologically very advanced." That wasn't enough for Sarah Palin, however, who sneered at the Obama administration's plans to conduct more studies before drilling in some areas. "My goodness, folks, these areas have been studied to death," she told the Southern Republican leadership conference in New Orleans, now just 11 days before the blowout. "Let's drill, baby, drill, not stall, baby, stall!" And there was much rejoicing.

In his congressional testimony, Hayward said: "We and the entire industry will learn from this terrible event." And one might well imagine that a catastrophe of this magnitude would indeed instill BP executives and the "Drill Now" crowd with a new sense of humility. There are, however, no signs that this is the case. The response to the disaster—at the corporate and governmental levels—has been rife with the precise brand of arrogance and overly sunny predictions that created the disaster in the first place.

The ocean is big, she can take it, we heard from Hayward in the early days. While spokesman John Curry insisted that hungry microbes would consume whatever oil was in the water system, because "nature has a way of helping the situation." But nature has not been playing along. The deep-sea gusher has bust out of all BP's top hats, containment domes, and junk shots. The ocean's winds and currents have made a mockery of the lightweight booms BP has laid out to absorb the oil. "We told them," said Byron Encalade, the president of the Louisiana Oysters Association. "The oil's gonna go over the booms or underneath the bottom." Indeed it did. The marine biologist Rick Steiner, who has been following the clean up closely, estimates that "70% or 80% of the booms are doing absolutely nothing at all."

And then there are the controversial chemical dispersants: more than 1.3 million gallons dumped with the company's trademark "What could go wrong?" attitude. As the angry residents at the Plaquemines Parish town hall rightly point out, few tests had been conducted, and there is scant research about what this unprecedented amount of dispersed oil will do to marine life. Nor is there a way to clean up the toxic mixture of oil and chemicals below the surface. Yes, fast multiplying microbes do devour underwater oil but in the process they also absorb the water's oxygen, creating a whole new threat to marine life.

BP had even dared to imagine that it could prevent unflattering images of oil-covered beaches and birds from escaping the disaster zone. When I was on the water with a TV crew, for instance, we were approached by another boat whose captain asked, "Y'all work for BP?" When we said no, the response—in the open ocean—was "You can't be here then." But of course these heavy-handed tactics, like all the others, have failed. There is simply too much oil in too many places. "You cannot tell God's air where to flow and go, and you can't tell water where to flow and go," I was told by Debra Ramirez. It was a lesson she had learned from living in Mossville, Louisiana, surrounded by 14 emission-spewing petrochemical plants, and watching illness spread from neighbour to neighbour.

Human limitation has been the one constant of this catastrophe. After two months, we still have no idea how much oil is flowing, nor when it will stop. The company's claim that it will complete relief wells by the end of August—repeated by Obama in his Oval Office address—is seen by many scientists as a bluff. The procedure is risky and could fail, and there is a real possibility that the oil could continue to leak for years.

The flow of denial shows no sign of abating either. Louisiana politicians indignantly oppose Obama's temporary freeze on deepwater drilling, accusing him of killing the one big industry left standing now that fishing and tourism are in crisis. Palin mused on Facebook that "No human endeavour is ever without risk," while Texas Republican congressman John Culberson described the disaster as a "statistical anomaly." By far the most sociopathic reaction, however, comes from veteran Washington commentator Llewellyn King: rather than turning away from big engineering risks, we should pause in "wonder that we can build machines so remarkable that they can lift the lid off the underworld."

MAKE THE BLEEDING STOP

Thankfully, many are taking a very different lesson from the disaster, standing not in wonder at humanity's power to reshape nature, but at our powerlessness to cope with the fierce natural forces we unleash. There is something else too. It is the feeling that the hole at the bottom of the ocean is more than an engineering accident or a broken machine. It is a violent wound in a living organism; that it is part of us. And thanks to BP's live camera feed, we can all watch the Earth's guts gush forth, in real time, 24 hours a day.

John Wathen, a conservationist with the Waterkeeper Alliance, was one of the few independent observers to fly over the spill in the early days of the disaster. After filming the thick red streaks of oil that the coast guard politely refers to as "rainbow sheen," he observed what many had felt: "The Gulf seems to be bleeding." This imagery comes up again and again in conversations and interviews. Monique Harden, an environmental rights lawyer in New Orleans, refuses to call the disaster an "oil spill" and instead says, "we are hemorrhaging." Others speak of the need to "make the bleeding stop." And I was personally struck, flying over the stretch of ocean where the Deepwater Horizon sank with the U.S. Coast Guard, that the swirling shapes the oil made in the ocean waves looked remarkably like cave drawings: a feathery lung gasping for air, eyes staring upwards, a prehistoric bird. Messages from the deep.

And this is surely the strangest twist in the Gulf coast saga: it seems to be waking us up to the reality that the Earth never was a machine. After 400 years of being declared dead, and in the middle of so much death, the Earth is coming alive.

The experience of following the oil's progress through the ecosystem is a kind of crash course in deep ecology. Every day we learn more about how what seems to be a terrible problem in one isolated part of the world actually radiates out in ways most of us could never have imagined. One day we learn that the oil could reach Cuba—then Europe. Next we hear that fishermen all the way up the Atlantic in Prince Edward Island, Canada, are worried because the Bluefin tuna they catch off their shores are born thousands of miles away in those oil-stained Gulf waters. And we learn, too, that for birds, the Gulf coast wetlands are the equivalent of a busy airport hub—everyone seems to have a stopover: 110 species of migratory songbirds and 75% of all migratory US waterfowl.

It's one thing to be told by an incomprehensible chaos theorist that a butterfly flapping its wings in Brazil can set off a tornado in Texas. It's another to watch chaos theory unfold before your eyes. Carolyn Merchant puts the lesson like this: "The problem as BP has tragically and belatedly discovered is that nature as an active force cannot be so confined." Predictable outcomes are unusual within ecological systems, while "unpredictable, chaotic events [are] usual." And just in case we still didn't get it, a few days ago, a bolt of lightning struck a BP ship like an exclamation mark, forcing it to suspend its containment efforts. And don't even mention what a hurricane would do to BP's toxic soup.

There is, it must be stressed, something uniquely twisted about this particular path to enlightenment. They say that Americans learn where foreign countries are by bombing them. Now it seems we are all learning about nature's circulatory systems by poisoning them.

In the late 90s, an isolated indigenous group in Colombia captured world headlines with an almost Avatar-esque conflict. From their remote home in the Andean cloud forests, the U'wa let it be known that if Occidental Petroleum carried out plans to drill for oil on their territory, they would commit mass ritual suicide by jumping off a cliff. Their elders explained that oil is part of ruiria, "the blood of Mother Earth." They believe that all life, including their own, flows from ruiria, so pulling out the oil would bring on their destruction. (Oxy eventually withdrew from the region, saying there wasn't as much oil as it had previously thought.)

Virtually all indigenous cultures have myths about gods and spirits living in the natural world—in rocks, mountains, glaciers, forests—as did European culture before the scientific revolution. Katja Neves, an anthropologist at Concordia University, points out that the practice serves a practical purpose. Calling the Earth "sacred" is another way of expressing humility in the face of forces we do not fully comprehend. When something is sacred, it demands that we proceed with caution. Even awe.

If we are absorbing this lesson at long last, the implications could be profound. Public support for increased offshore drilling is dropping precipitously, down 22% from the peak of the "Drill Now" frenzy. The issue is not dead, however. It is only a matter of time before the Obama administration announces that, thanks to ingenious new technology and tough new regulations, it is now perfectly safe to drill in the deep sea, even in the Arctic, where an under-ice clean up would be infinitely more complex than the one underway in the Gulf. But perhaps this time we won't be so easily reassured, so quick to gamble with the few remaining protected havens.

Same goes for geoengineering. As climate change negotiations wear on, we should be ready to hear more from Dr. Steven Koonin, Obama's undersecretary of energy for science. He is one of the leading proponents of the idea that climate change can be combated with techno tricks like releasing sulphate and aluminium particles into the atmosphere—and of course it's all perfectly safe, just like Disneyland! He also happens to be BP's former chief scientist, the man who just 15 months ago was still overseeing the technology behind BP's supposedly safe charge into deepwater drilling. Maybe this time we will opt not to let the good doctor experiment with the physics and chemistry of the Earth, and choose instead to reduce our consumption and shift to renewable energies that have the virtue that, when they fail, they fail small. As U.S. comedian Bill Maher put it, "You know what happens when windmills collapse into the sea? A splash."

The most positive possible outcome of this disaster would be not only an acceleration of renewable energy sources like wind, but a full embrace of the precautionary principle in science. The mirror opposite of Hayward's "If you knew you could not fail" credo, the precautionary principle holds that "when an activity raises threats of harm to the environment or human health" we tread carefully, as if failure were possible, even likely. Perhaps we can even get Hayward a new desk plaque to contemplate as he signs compensation cheques. "You act like you know, but you don't know."

Journalist Wayne Drash wrote this piece for CNN in June 2010, at the height of the BP oil disaster in the Gulf of Mexico. Drash uses the plight of the brown pelican to explain the effects of environmental disasters caused by humans on the natural world.

THE BROWN PELICAN: LONG A SYMBOL OF SURVIVAL

By Wayne Drash

Long before the brown pelican came to symbolize the tragedy of the Gulf oil spill, the giant bird stood for something much greater: survival against all odds.

The state bird of Louisiana was nearly wiped out by pesticides in the 1950s and 1960s. Yet after decades of conservation efforts, the brown pelican just last year was removed from the endangered species list.

"At a time when so many species of wildlife are threatened, we once in a while have an opportunity to celebrate an amazing success story," Interior Secretary Ken Salazar declared on November 11. "Today is such a day. The brown pelican is back."

Now, eight months later, Louisiana Governor Bobby Jindal stands on the deck of a boat near Pelican Island off the Louisiana coast. He's surveying efforts to protect the state's wetlands. He's ordered the National Guard to begin building barriers in the ocean to try to stop the oil from reaching shore. Yet Jindal pauses to talk about the brown pelican. The recent images of pelicans, coated in BP oil like grotesque statues, have taken on the symbolism of the spill. Louisiana has long been known as the "Pelican State," with the bird gracing the state flag.

"Here's what's really sad," Jindal said. "For every one of those mother adult pelicans you're saving, there are many more back there that you can't get to. And for every mother pelican you're saving, there may be a nest, there may be eggs that can't be saved. And that's the tragedy in this: That for every animal we see, what's this oil doing to their young? What's this oil doing to their life cycles?"

The recovery of the pelicans, before the spill, was largely attributed to the ban of the toxic chemical DDT in 1972. The pesticide traveled down the Mississippi River and into the Gulf of Mexico. Three species were most affected: the brown pelican, the bald eagle and peregrine falcon. A component of DDT accumulated in each of those birds and, as a result, it affected the strength of the eggs they laid.

"The result was that you had thinner egg shells in the nest. During incubation, all the species had the tendency to break the eggs more easily," said Dr. Doug Inkey, a senior scientist for the National Wildlife Federation. "This resulted in a huge population decline in all three species."

The bald eagle, peregrine falcon and brown pelican were all listed on the endangered species list. In the case of the brown pelican, wildlife officials in Louisiana and Florida teamed up to help save the bird over a 13-year period. A total of 1,276 young pelicans were captured in Florida and then released at three sites in southeastern Louisiana, according to the Interior Department.

"When their populations were low, we brought in those brown pelicans from Florida," Jindal said. "Now, when we capture them oiled, clean them up and rehabilitate them, we have to release them back in Florida to get away from this oil."

The U.S. Fish and Wildlife Service has deployed more than 450 people across the Gulf to respond to the nation's worst environmental disaster. As of Monday, the oil threatened 36 National Wildlife Refuges. Nearly 1,200 birds have been saved, including 728 in Louisiana.

Ron Britton of the Fish and Wildlife Service gave a CNN crew a tour of the marsh islands near Grand Isle, Louisiana, a prime breeding ground where oiled pelicans have been spotted. "What you're trying to do is get in and get those as quick as you can," Britton told CNN's Anderson Cooper. "But the ones you're missing have less chance each night you can't get back. And the ones we don't get back, we're pretty sure are going somewhere and not surviving."

Oil affects pelicans in various ways. The birds' feathers interlock in a way that helps regulate cooling and, when oil soaks their feathers, the birds lose the ability to do that, biologists say. "Brown pelicans dive into the water for fish. As they break the water, that's one of the ways they contact the oil. Then, once it's on their feathers, the birds preen daily," said Jennifer Coulson, president of the Orleans Audubon Society. "When they're preening, they ingest all the BP oil. And so, that's another way they get sick and die."

Inkey of the National Wildlife Federation added, "When they get back to their nests, then they rub some of the oil from their chests to their eggs—and oil on eggs is not a good mix. It's usually deadly for the developing embryo." Inkey recently visited a brown pelican-nesting habitat along the Louisiana coast. Hundreds of the birds lived together in nests about 6 feet high in mangrove trees along the shore. There were two layers of protective booms surrounding the island that were "close to being worthless."

"We saw more oil inside the booms than we saw outside the booms," he said. "It was surrounded by a bathtub ring of oil." His first thought: What's going to happen to the pelicans this year? "This is the worst-case scenario: It's during breeding season," he said. "We're likely to lose a whole generation of young of many different species. ... It only takes once for a bird to really get messed up in oil for it to have an effect on the nesting success."

He and other biologists said it's far too early to know the full effect of the oil spill on the larger population of brown pelicans—and whether the bird would ever make it back to the endangered species list. "It would be premature to suggest that," Inkey said.

Biologists said the pelican—known for its long beak with a hooked tip and its 6-foot wingspan—is better equipped to survive than smaller birds that ingest oil in greater proportion to their size. In addition, there are five species of sea turtles in the Gulf, and all are endangered or threatened. "A sea turtle hatchling does not stand a chance," Inkey said.

Regardless, it's a dire situation for all types of wildlife in the region, biologists said. Yet it was the images of the oil-soaked pelicans that brought home the scope of the disaster—and its potential devastating consequences. The birds survived DDT, the constant erosion of Louisiana wetlands and Hurricane Katrina.

Inkey already had returned from his visit when the photos first appeared. "I got sick in my stomach," he said. "I had seen oiled pelicans, but not like that. The ones I saw were simply gray. These were just heartbreaking." He paused. "How do you explain a picture like that to young children and get them to understand that this is something, although unintentional, that man caused?"

***

CNN's Dugald McConnell and Brian Todd contributed to this report.

Explore

"A Hole in the World" was published in June 2010. In the time since then, what changes have occurred in the Gulf region with respect to the BP oil spill? How many gallons of oil leaked into the water before the leak was plugged? What is the current state of the ecosystem affected by the spill? How successful have the recovery efforts been? What communities and professions have been displaced or put out of work by the disaster, and how has BP responded to the communities affected by the spill?

Conduct some online or library research (or if possible, interview some experts) about how rescue crews in the Gulf capture and clean oil coated pelicans and write an explanatory essay that explains the process to a non-expert reader. A quick search online will turn up videos of the cleaning process. After you've described the process, do some more research so that you can discuss what happens to the pelicans after they have been released.

DENALI/DENIAL

By Chris Jordan

This image (and the detail at right) is part of artist Chris Jordan's series called "Running the Numbers: An American Self-Portrait (2006 - 2009)." The 60-inch-by-75-inch piece depicts 24,000 logos from the GMC Yukon Denali, equal to six weeks of sales of that model SUV in 2004. For more information see the next page.

You can find the "Denali/Denial" image (from page 81) and the rest of the "Running the Numbers" series at artist Chris Jordan's website, available at http://www.chrisjordan.com. According to Jordan, "'Running the Numbers' looks at contemporary American culture through the austere lens of statistics. Each image portrays a specific quantity of something: fifteen million sheets of office paper (five minutes of paper use); 106,000 aluminum cans (thirty seconds of can consumption) and so on." Go to Jordan's website and spend some time studying the images in the "Running the Numbers" series (make sure you click on the images to zoom in) before moving on to the other writing prompts below.

Jordan says that, in "[e]mploying themes such as the near versus the far, and the one versus the many, I hope to raise some questions about the roles and responsibilities we each play as individuals in a collective that is increasingly enormous, incomprehensible, and overwhelming." What do you think Jordan is saying about our individual and collective roles and responsibilities with "Denali/Denial"? Explain your response.

Collaborate

Jordan says of the "Running the Numbers" series: "My hope is that images representing these quantities might have a different effect than the raw numbers alone, such as we find daily in articles and books. Statistics can feel abstract and anesthetizing, making it difficult to connect with and make meaning of 3.6 million SUV sales in one year, for example, or 2.3 million Americans in prison, or 32,000 breast augmentation surgeries in the U.S. every month." Working with a small group, discuss a suitable subject for inclusion in "Running the Numbers" (keep in mind that this must involve not just data, but also a visually arresting way to represent that data). Then, with your group, write a letter to Jordan suggesting your plan.

Christie Matheson says she wrote the 2008 book Green Chic: Saving the Earth in Style *to offer guidance "to anyone who wants to live greener, and do it with style." In order to save the planet, she says in her introduction, we all need to embrace "the fabulousness of green living." The following piece is an excerpt from her book.*

excerpts from

GREEN CHIC: SAVING THE EARTH IN STYLE

BY CHRISTIE MATHESON

GREEN IS THE NEW BLACK

I recently read an article that advised readers to stop buying things if they wanted to lessen their negative impact on the environment. Seriously, that was the advice. Stop shopping for everything except absolute essentials like food and toilet paper, and make do with what you already have. Um...yeah, *right*. True, consuming just about anything is eco-detrimental (production, packaging, and shipping all take their toll) but that doesn't mean I'm going to wear last year's designer denim for the next eight seasons. Please.

Here's a more realistic plan: Be thoughtful about the clothes and accessories you buy and the habits you use when buying and taking care of them. (This chapter's got tips on how to do that.) Along with the process of lightening your environmental footprint, there's a surprising added bonus—you'll probably cut way down on buyer's remorse. My "why the hell is that in my closet?" purchases are close to zero since I've started being an eco-conscious shopper. I get more compliments and "*where* did you find that?" questions from my friends, including my fashion editor friends.

Keep in mind that this chapter is *not* about getting rid of all the "non-green" clothing you own and buying an entirely new ecofriendly wardrobe. That wouldn't be green at all. But when you do get a craving for something fabulous, here are a bunch of ideas to help you become a greener fashionista.

Because, although going green should never be just a fashion statement, green really is the new black.

EDIT YOUR CLOSET

One of the first things a personal shopper or personal stylist—you have both of those, right?—will do for you is go through your closet and pare it down so it only contains things you love, love, love to wear. (I know this not because I have a staff of stylists and shoppers, but because I've interviewed them for fashion stories and paid attention, so I could use their advice and not have to pay for it.) There are definitely perks to my job. Sometimes, anyway.

The idea is that if you love *everything* in your closet—even if you end up with a third of the clothes you had before you started the editing process—you'll have a much easier time getting dressed in the morning and you'll always look (and believe that you look) stunning.

This is definitely a less-is-more situation. Crap in your closet—pieces that don't fit, don't flatter, or make you feel like you're wearing a tent—distracts from the amazing stuff that's already in there. And if you're distracted from the amazing stuff that's already in there, you might think you need to go on a shopping spree to save you from wardrobe hatred. This is not a green solution. Edit first, 'kay?

To get started, go through *every single item* in your closet. If you hate it and you know it, put it into the NO pile. (At the end, please donate said NO pile to a women's shelter, bring it to a clothing swap, or consign it. Do not toss it into the trash so it makes its way to a landfill. Thank you.) If you love it and you know it, put it into a YES pile. I do not believe in a MAYBE pile—you know you're just going to keep it, and then what's the point? If you're not sure about a piece, try it on and assess how it looks, how it makes you feel, and what you can wear it with. If you look smokin' and you can think of an upcoming situation where you'll want to wear it, and you have stuff that looks good with it, it's a yes. If you don't like how it looks, or you know, realistically that you just won't wear it, it's a no. Don't cry. Let it go. You don't love it, and it certainly doesn't love you back.

If something you love is in a state of disrepair, assess whether it can be fixed. If so, *get it fixed* instead of buying a new one. If not, say goodbye. And learn from the experience: Take care of the clothing you love, and be fastidious about getting it straightened up at the first sign of an unraveling thread, missing button, or wee little hole.

Finally, don't stop editing. Go in early (before malaise sets in) and often, and weed out anything not stupendous. And the next time you shop (and forever thereafter), don't buy *anything* you think might wind up in a NO pile. It will only get in the way of your relationship with the clothes you love. (The ones in which you are so chic. Admit it.)

BAG BAGS, COMPLETELY

Remember those *Sex and the City* scenes where Carrie Bradshaw would come breezing through her door and drop an armload of Manolo Blahnik and Barneys bags? I'm not going to suggest you give up shopping sprees altogether, but it's a good idea to avoid that kind of bag orgy. Shopping bags—both paper and plastic—are bigger environmental offenders than you might realize. I mention this briefly and suggest popping little purchases into your purse. But I think you're ready to take it to the next level. Are you with me? We should bang knuckles or something right now. Instead I'll explain why.

Let's start with plastic: According to the Environmental Protection Agency (EPA), close to a trillion plastic bags are used worldwide each year. The United States uses about one hundred billion of those. That's—yikes—almost one thousand plastic bags per year per U.S. household—meaning even one household opting out of plastic bags makes a noticeable dent. It takes twelve million barrels of oil to produce the plastic bags the United States alone uses each year. Fewer than 3 percent of plastic bags are recycled—meaning they end up in landfills (where they can take hundreds of years to degrade) and often in streams, rivers, and oceans, where they choke and poison about one hundred thousand whales, birds, and turtles each year and act as rafts to carry foreign species to places where they can do damage to existing ecosystems. What's more, most plastic bags are made from polyethylene, which is derived from petroleum or natural gas (you know by now these are nonrenewable resources). When they do break down—and they don't safely or completely biodegrade—they release toxic chemicals into the earth's air, soil, and water.

And then there's paper: I used to think these were better for the environment than plastic because they are biodegradable. Nope. Making ten billion paper bags (about the number of grocery bags Americans use in a year) requires fourteen million trees to be cut down. And then manufacturing them, which involves heating wood chips in a chemical solution at a high temperature, takes four times more energy than manufacturing plastic bags, and produces 70 percent more air pollutants and 50 percent more water pollutants. Only 20 percent of paper bags are recycled, and they take up nine times as much space in landfills as plastic bags do.

If everyone in New York City alone used *just one* less shopping bag per year, it would eliminate 5 million pounds of waste (counting the bags themselves, the tree waste, and the stuff that goes into making them) and save the city $250,000 in disposal costs. Bags that are a hybrid of paper and plastic (like so many fancy laminated shopping bags are) are the worst, because they are rarely recyclable.

The solution? Don't use shopping bags at all.

This is an easy green shopping strategy to employ. Every single time you head out to go shopping (whether you're just browsing or picking up a bottle of wine and a wedge of cheese or going for a serious wardrobe or home overhaul), be prepared with a sturdy, reusable bag. I'm a huge fan of the L.L. Bean Boat & Tote bags, and I have them in every size (and several colors). If uber-elegant is the only thing that works for you, consider this the perfect excuse to invest in that beautiful bag you've been coveting. You'd be doing it to save the earth! Keep it right by your door and use it exclusively for shopping, so it's always clean, empty, and waiting for you.

Tip: Let the sales person know—nicely!—as soon as you get to the register that you don't need a bag. That way they won't beat you to the punch and start swaddling your purchase in tissue paper and ribbon while you're looking down to hunt for your credit card.

OPT FOR ORGANIC COTTON

It's easy to assume that all natural fibers, including cotton, are ecofriendly. That's what I used to think, and I was probably even kind of snooty about it. Turns out I was off the mark. Some natural fibers are fantastic, but conventionally grown cotton is not. It's actually an environmental disaster.

Here's why: Growing conventional cotton is *the* most pesticide intensive farming process in the world. Only about 3 percent of the world's farmland is used for growing cotton, yet conventional cotton growth uses about 24 percent of all pesticides—which permeate the air, damage the soil, and seep into the water supply. Every pound of cotton (which is about how much it takes to make one T-shirt) is sprayed with a third of a pound of pesticides—and a total of 50 million pounds of pesticides are used on cotton in the United States alone. Then there are the chemical fertilizers—more than 2 billion pounds (142 pounds per acre) are used annually to grow conventional cotton in the United States.

By the way, all those pesticides and fertilizers in the cotton fields translate to about a third of a cup of chemical (which include such known cancer-causing agents as cyanide, dicofol, naled, propargite, and trifluralin) remaining in your cute little cotton tee. Which you're probably wearing right next to your skin.

Organic cotton is grown without any pesticides or chemical fertilizers, meaning none of that seeps into the air, the water, the soil, or your skin. The organic cotton industry is growing rapidly (the women's apparel segment of it is growing the fastest, at about 35 percent per year) and it's getting easier and easier to find organic cotton in the form of luxe goods such as silky soft tees. Plus, it's appearing in totally affordable products such as American Apparel (americanapparel.com) tees (around $15) and sexy little thongs ($8), Wal-Mart pajamas (about $12), and Danskin yoga pants ($14-ish).

Shopping for organic cotton at Wal-Mart doesn't excite you? Okay, you can also find such fashion forward designers as Loomstate (organic jeans designed by Rogan Gregory; loomstate.org), Edun (the cutting-edge label founded by Bono's wife, Ali Hewson; edun.com), Linda Loudermilk (some Hollywood celebs wore her to the Oscars; lindaloudermilk.com), and my personal favorite, Stewart+Brown (a California-based line featuring perfectly cut, expensive-but-worth-it tees, skirts, and sweaters; stewartbrown.com). More designer denim options include the incredibly flattering jeans from Del Forte (delforte.com) and the new organic denim line from everybody's favorite maker of jeans, Levi's (levi.com).

Tip: Try it out! For a short period of time, like two months, commit to buying only organic if you're picking up any item of cotton clothing (jeans, tees, underwear). You'll probably find yourself wasting less money on cheap trendy items that you'll never wear—and you'll love the way the fabric feels next to your body. And you may get other benefits: Will tends to give me more spontaneous backrubs when I'm wearing an organic cotton tee. Then there are the compliments—I was wearing a Stewart+Brown organic cotton skirt at dinner the other night and my friend Kate couldn't stop touching it. Of course she asked where I got it because it was so soft and such a great skirt, and she wanted one. I found it at Envi (shopenvi.com), a new eco-boutique on Newbury Street in Boston that has a great online shop as well. (Stewart+Brown is also sold at boutiques all over the country—check stewartbrown.com to find a retail location near you.) Anyway, chances are you'll be a total convert after your self-imposed only-organic restricted period, but if not, you can always go back to conventional for some of your purchases—just try to buy organic whenever it's convenient.

Shopping strategy: Is there a boutique near you that carries chic organic cotton pieces? Let them know you love it, and tell your friends to support their efforts, too.

Tip: Just because a cotton item is a natural color doesn't mean it's organic. I know you already figured that out, but I just read an article about "green" fashion in a certain high-end lifestyle magazine, and the page was filled with clothes in shades of cream, tan, and taupe—but not even half of them were organic. Read the label. If it's organic, it will say so.

GET GREEN BLING

I hate to be the one to tell you this, but diamonds are not a green girl's best friend. And all that's gold is *not* green. Sorry.

Unfortunately, obtaining the natural elements—diamonds, other gemstones, platinum—that go into traditional beautiful jewelry is not an environmentally beautiful practice. Accessing such materials requires mining, which consumes huge amounts of energy, releases pollutants and greenhouse gases into the air, allows toxic chemicals to seep into groundwater, damages land and speeds up erosion, and generates an unbelievable amount of waste. The use of chemicals such as cyanide and mercury to separate gold from rock is a terrible health hazard for miners who are breathing it in as well as being an environmental hazard.

Mining is also associated with many socially devastating practices, especially in African countries such as Angola and Sierra Leone, where the diamond industry has been known to fund violence against innocent civilians. The United Nations calls these conflict diamonds, and they define them as "diamonds that originate from areas controlled by forces or factions opposed to legitimate and internationally recognized governments, and are used to fund military action in opposition to those governments, or in contravention of the decisions of the Security Council." This is too huge a topic to address in great detail here—but if you're going to buy a new diamond, make sure it comes with a certificate of origin, and is certified conflict-free. Keep reading to find out where to buy.

Mining is not a small industry. In the United States, mining consumes about 5 percent of the total electricity the country uses. In countries such as South Africa, where there's a richer concentration of "valuable" materials, the consumption is much higher—around 25 percent of total energy consumption. Not all this mining is for jewelry—but a surprisingly large amount of it is: Of the 2,500 tons of gold that are mined each year, for example, 80 percent of it goes into jewelry. And according to Oxfam America, the production of one little 18-karet ring that weighs less than an ounce creates more than 20 tons of mine waste. One ring.

Fear not: This doesn't mean you have to stop getting jewelry as a gift (or treating yourself to that perfect bauble to celebrate...whatever). There are eco-chic jewelers out there making gorgeous pieces—not the clunky beaded stuff you might imagine green types have to wear. There are sparkly rings, sleek bracelets, and shiny earrings made from recycled gold and platinum and "created" diamonds and gemstones—synthetic stones that match the quality of the natural kind are now available from high-end companies such as Apollo (apollodiamond.com). Trust me (the gal who doesn't particularly like synthetics): They can be gorgeous.

GreenKarat (greenkarat.com) uses synthetic diamonds and gems as well as recycled gold and platinum in everything from minimalist diamond-studded wedding bands to eye-popping triple stone rings. Brilliant Earth (brilliantearth.com) offers engagement rings and wedding bands made from recycled metals and conflict-free diamonds (these are my personal favorites); Leber Jeweler (leberjeweler.com) has an Earthwise line of classic diamond studs, engagement rings, and gemstone pendants made of reclaimed metals and conflict-free stones. And—ready for some happy news?—Tiffany (tiffany.com) is making great strides toward ecofriendliness. Their diamonds are certified conflict-free (and their efforts in promoting this have led to more stringent oversight of the diamond industry in general), they mine metals responsibly, they are part of the No Dirty Gold campaign, and they don't use coral because its harvesting can damage marine habitats. Oh, and those little blue boxes are made from Forest Stewardship Council-certified paper.

Another alternative—one that demands an even smaller ecological price than even ecofriendly new gems—is to choose antique jewelry. Made from metals and stones mined decades (or centuries) ago, it's an extremely low-impact choice and a great way to find pieces that won't look like something everyone (or anyone) you know is wearing. Or you could take a stone that your mother or grandmother had (hey, it'll have even more meaning) and have your jeweler set it into a ring or pendant for you. But now you need to find a jeweler that's willing to use (and knows how to get) recycled metals, huh? Contact Ethical Metalsmiths (ethicalmetalsmiths.org) to find a jeweler near you. Or recycle your old jewelry. If there's a piece you don't wear anymore, have a jeweler melt it down and create something you actually want to wear.

According to Matheson, fashion forward designers like Loomstate, Edun, and Stewart+Brown are making an effort to use organic cotton in their designs. Using the web and your library's resources, research some of the eco friendly trends in the fashion industry. Beyond the use of organic cotton, what are some of the green strategies fashion houses employ? What environmental strains do these strategies hope to alleviate?

In her introduction to *Green Chic*, Matheson informs us that she's "not a veteran environmentalist" and that she enjoys "certain creature comforts" such as taking hot showers and having a killer wardrobe. What she's developing with these claims is a particular persona or ethos that allows us to identify with her as an author. Based on the information she tells us about herself, her tone throughout the excerpt, and the stylistic choices she makes in her writing, how would you characterize Matheson's ethos? How does this persona work to persuade us? Does it make you want to listen more carefully to what she has to say or less? Who do you imagine is her target audience?

Write a short essay in which you compare the authorial persona or ethos of Matheson to that of Colin Beavan, the author of *No Impact Man*, whose excerpt can be found on page 99. In your essay, consider the following questions: What different approaches do the authors take in terms of developing their authorial personae? Why do you think they make these choices? Which author do you take more seriously? Why? Which author do you think is a better advocate for "going green"?

Shannon Hayes—the author of Radical Homemakers, The Farmer and the Grill, *and* The Grassfed Gourmet Cookbook*—wrote this article in February 2010 for* YES! magazine, *a national, nonprofit media organization that, according to its website, "fuses powerful ideas with practical actions."*

MEET THE RADICAL HOMEMAKERS

BY SHANNON HAYES

Long before we could pronounce Betty Friedan's last name, Americans from my generation felt her impact. Many of us born in the mid-1970s learned from our parents and our teachers that women no longer needed to stay home, that there were professional opportunities awaiting us. In my own school experience, homemaking, like farming, gained a reputation as a vocation for the scholastically impaired. Those of us with academic promise learned that we could do whatever we put our minds to, whether it was conquering the world or saving the world. I was personally interested in saving the world. That path eventually led me to conclude that homemaking would play a major role toward achieving that goal.

My own farming background led me to pursue advanced degrees in the field of sustainable agriculture, with a powerful interest in the local food movement. By the time my Ph.D. was conferred, I was married, and I was in a state of confusion. The more I understood about the importance of small farms and the nutritional, ecological, and social value of local food, the more I questioned the value of a 9-to-5 job. If my husband and I both worked and had children, it appeared that our family's ecological impact would be considerable. We'd require two cars, professional wardrobes, convenience foods to make up for lost time in the kitchen ... and we'd have to buy, rather than produce, harvest, and store, our own food.

The economics didn't work out, either. When we crunched the numbers, our gross incomes from two careers would have been high, but the cost of living was also considerable, especially when daycare was figured into the calculation. Abandoning the job market, we re-joined my parents on our small grass-fed livestock farm and became homemakers. For almost ten years now, we've been able to eat locally and organically, support local businesses, avoid big box stores, save money, and support a family of four on less than $45,000 per year.

Wondering if my family was a freaky aberration to the conventional American culture, I decided to post a notice on my webpage, looking to connect with other ecologically minded homemakers. My fingers trembled on the keyboard as I typed the notice. What, exactly, would be the repercussions for taking a pro-homemaker stand and seeking out others? Was encouraging a Radical Homemaking movement going to unravel all the social advancements that have been made in the last 40-plus years? Women, after all, have been the homemakers since the beginning of time. Or so I thought.

THE ORIGINS OF HOMEMAKING: A VOCATION FOR BOTH SEXES

Upon further investigation, I learned that the household did not become the "woman's sphere" until the Industrial Revolution. A search for the origin of the word *housewife* traces it back to the thirteenth century, as the feudal period was coming to an end in Europe and the first signs of a middle class were popping up. Historian Ruth Schwartz Cowan explains that housewives were wedded to husbands, whose name came from *hus*, an old spelling of *house*, and *bonded*. Husbands were bonded to houses, rather than to lords. Housewives and husbands were free people, who owned their own homes and lived off their land. While there was a division of labor among the sexes in these early households, there was also an equal distribution of domestic work. Once the Industrial Revolution happened, however, things changed. Men left the household to work for wages, which were then used to purchase goods and services that they were no longer home to provide. Indeed, the men were the first to lose their domestic skills as successive generations forgot how to butcher the family hog, how to sew leather, how to chop firewood.

As the Industrial Revolution forged on and crossed the ocean to America, men and women eventually stopped working together to provide for their household sustenance. They developed their separate spheres—man in the factory, woman in the home. The more a man worked outside the home, the more the household would have to buy in order to have needs met. Soon the factories were able to fabricate products to supplant the housewives' duties as well. The housewife's primary function ultimately became chauffeur and consumer. The household was no longer a unit of production. It was a unit of consumption.

HOUSEWIFE'S SYNDROME

The effect on the American housewife was devastating. In 1963, Betty Friedan published *The Feminine Mystique*, documenting for the first time "the problem that has no name," Housewife's Syndrome, where American girls grew up fantasizing about finding their husbands, buying their dream homes and appliances, popping out babies, and living happily ever after. In truth, pointed out Friedan, happily-ever-after never came. Countless women suffered from depression and nervous breakdowns as they faced the endless meaningless tasks of shopping and driving children hither and yon. They never had opportunities to fulfill their highest potential, to challenge themselves, to feel as though they were truly contributing to society beyond wielding the credit card to keep the consumer culture humming. Friedan's book sent women to work in droves. And corporate America seized upon a golden opportunity to secure a cheaper workforce and offer countless products to use up their paychecks.

Before long, the second family income was no longer an option. In the minds of many, it was a necessity. Homemaking, like eating organic foods, seemed a luxury to be enjoyed only by those wives whose husbands garnered substantial earnings, enabling them to drive their children to school rather than put them on a bus, enroll them in endless enrichment activities, oversee their educational careers, and prepare them for entry into elite colleges in order to win a leg-up in a competitive workforce. At the other extreme, homemaking was seen as the realm of the ultra-religious, where women accepted the role of Biblical "Help Meets" to their husbands. They cooked, cleaned, toiled, served and remained silent and powerless. My husband and I fell into neither category, and I suspected there were more like us.

MEET THE RADICAL HOMEMAKERS

I was right. I received hundreds of letters from rural, suburban, and city folks alike. Some ascribed to specific religious faiths, others did not. As long as the home showed no signs of domination or oppression, I was interested in learning more about them. I selected twenty households from my pile, plotted them on a map across the United States, and set about visiting each of them to see what homemaking could look like when men and women shared both power and responsibility. Curious to see if Radical Homemaking was a venture suited to more than just women in married couples, I visited with single parents, stay-at-home dads, widows, and divorcées. I spent time in families with and without children.

A glance into America's past suggests that homemaking could play a big part in addressing the ecological, economic and social crises of our present time. Homemakers have played a powerful role during several critical periods in our nation's history. By making use of locally available resources, they made the boycotts leading up to the American Revolution possible. They played a critical role in the foundational civic education required to launch a young democratic nation. They were driving forces behind both the abolition and suffrage movements.

Homemakers today could have a similar influence. The Radical Homemakers I interviewed had chosen to make family, community, social justice, and the health of the planet the governing principles of their lives. They rejected any form of labor or the expenditure of any resource that did not honor these tenets. For about 5,000 years, our culture has been hostage to a form of organization by domination that fails to honor our living systems, under which "he who holds the gold makes the rules." By contrast, the Radical Homemakers are using life skills and relationships as replacements for gold, on the premise that he or she who doesn't need the gold can change the rules. The greater one's domestic skills, be they to plant a garden, grow tomatoes on an apartment balcony, mend a shirt, repair an appliance, provide one's own entertainment, cook and preserve a local harvest, or care for children and loved ones, the less dependent one is on the gold.

By virtue of these skills, the Radical Homemakers I interviewed were building a great bridge from our existing extractive economy—where corporate wealth has been regarded as the foundation of economic health, where mining our Earth's resources and exploiting our international neighbors have been acceptable costs of doing business—to a life serving economy, where the goal is, in the words of David Korten, to generate a living for all, rather than a killing for a few; where our resources are sustained, our waters are kept clean, our air pure, and families and can lead meaningful lives. In situations where one person was still required to work out of the home in the conventional extractive economy, homemakers were able to redirect the family's financial, social and temporal resources toward building the life-serving economy. In most cases, however, the homemakers' skills were so considerable that, while members of the household might hold jobs (more often than not they ran their own businesses), the financial needs of the family were so small that no one in the family was forced to accept any employment that did not honor the four tenets of family, community, social justice and ecological sustainability.

While all the families had some form of income that entered their lives, they were not a privileged set by any means. Most of the families I interviewed were living with a sense of abundance at about 200 percent of the federal poverty level. That's a little over $40,000 for a family of four, about 37 percent below the national median family income, and 45 percent below the median income for married couple families. Some lived on considerably less, few had appreciably more. Not surprisingly, those with the lowest incomes had mastered the most domestic skills and had developed the most innovative approaches to living.

RETHINKING THE IMPOSSIBLE

The Radical Homemakers were skilled at the mental exercise of rethinking the "givens" of our society and coming to the following conclusions: nobody (who matters) cares what (or if) you drive; housing does not have to cost more than a single moderate income can afford (and can even cost less); it is okay to accept help from family and friends, to let go of the perceived ideal of independence and strive instead for interdependence; health can be achieved without making monthly payments to an insurance company; child care is not a fixed cost; education can be acquired for free; and retirement is possible, regardless of income.

As for domestic skills, the range of talents held by these households was as varied as the day is long. Many kept gardens, but not all. Some gardened on city rooftops, some on country acres, some in suburban yards. Some were wizards at car and appliance repairs. Others could sew. Some could build and fix houses; some kept livestock. Others crafted furniture, played music, or wrote. All could cook. (Really well, as my waistline will attest.) None of them could do everything. No one was completely self-sufficient, an independent island separate from the rest of the world. Thus the universal skills that they all possessed were far more complex than simply knowing how to can green beans or build a root cellar. In order to make it as homemakers, these people had to be wizards at nurturing relationships and working with family and community. They needed an intimate understanding of the life-serving economy, where a paycheck is not always exchanged for all services rendered. They needed to be their own teachers—to pursue their educations throughout life, forever learning new ways to do more, create more, give more.

In addition, the happiest among them were successful at setting realistic expectations for themselves. They did not live in impeccably clean houses on manicured estates. They saw their homes as living systems and accepted the flux, flow, dirt, and chaos that are a natural part of that. They were masters at redefining pleasure not as something that should be bought in the consumer marketplace, but as something that could be created, no matter how much or how little money they had in their pockets. And above all, they were fearless. They did not let themselves be bullied by the conventional ideals regarding money, status, or material possessions. These families did not see their homes as a refuge from the world. Rather, each home was the center for social change, the starting point from which a better life would ripple out for everyone.

Home is where the great change will begin. It is not where it ends. Once we feel sufficiently proficient with our domestic skills, few of us will be content to simply practice them to the end of our days. Many of us will strive for more, to bring more beauty to the world, to bring about greater social change, to make life better for our neighbors, to contribute our creative powers to the building of a new, brighter, more sustainable, and happier future. That is precisely the great work we should all be tackling. If we start by focusing our energies on our domestic lives, we will do more than reduce our ecological impact and help create a living for all. We will craft a safe, nurturing place from which this great creative work can happen.

Hayes is the host of two websites, grassfedcooking.com and radicalhomemakers.com. Choose one of these sites, take some time to explore its contents, and write a rhetorical analysis of the site you've chosen. Who do you think Hayes identifies as her audience? How does she appeal to her readers?

According to Hayes, radical homemakers subvert the housewife syndrome described by Betty Friedan in 1963. How do they accomplish this? How are the radical homemakers different than the homemakers Freidan describes?

Write an essay in which you compare the environmental or "green" identity described by Matheson in "*Green Chic*" and in Hayes' "Meet the Radical Homemakers." What are the primary values in each? Do these seemingly different approaches have anything in common?

Colin Beavan is the author of three books, including 2009's No Impact Man, *for which this piece served as the epilogue. In the book, Beavan explains his project this way: "For one year, my wife [Michelle], baby daughter [Isabella], and I, while residing in the middle of New York City, attempted to live life without making any net impact on the environment." He writes regularly about his experiment to help save the planet, and other environmental issues, at www.noimpactman.com.*

LIFE AFTER THE YEAR WITHOUT TOILET PAPER

By Colin Beavan

Here are the questions I get asked most often about the No Impact project:

1. What was the hardest part?
2. What aspects of the lifestyle did you keep?
3. How did the project change you?
4. What did you use instead of toilet paper?

Here are the questions I still ask myself:

1. With scientists expecting thousands of species to become extinct if the planet warms substantially, how do we make sure that we are not one of them?
2. In other words, how do we save the planet?
3. Will I ever—God help me—live down the toilet-paper thing?

We switched the lights back on just before Christmas, 2007. Thanks to the long-distance travel moratorium of the No Impact project, Michelle hadn't been back to Minneapolis to visit her family for more than a year. We planned to go for the holiday, but to avoid the excessive carbon emissions associated with air travel, we figured we'd take the train.

Then we did the research. It would take two days each way (at an average speed of twenty-five miles per hour). We'd have to get a roomette, since we couldn't imagine fellow coach passengers enjoying the energy that would pour out of Isabella during two restless days on a train. And, to top things off, it would cost $2,500 for the three of us. By comparison, the three of us could get from New York to Minneapolis, and back, by air for only about $1,000.

That clinched it. Although Europe boasts high-speed trains that average 120 miles per hour, here in the United States, practical, low-impact travel is not yet available. Michelle and Isabella would take the plane.

An eco-car service took them to the airport by Prius, but not me.

"Do you feel weird getting on a plane?" Michelle had asked me.

"Yes," I said.

"Then you don't have to come."

I just couldn't bring myself to climb on a plane within days of the No Impact project ending.

So I rattle around our apartment in New York by myself for the week. I'm disoriented. I find myself sitting in the living room at night, begrudging myself the use of electric light, even though the bulbs are compact fluorescent. I will only let myself have one lamp on at a time.

I feel dumb for being stingy with the lights. But also I feel like a hypocrite for having lights on that I don't truly need. It's strange. Like turning a light on or off is some sort of a moral quandary.

My problem is that I have been living for a year under the yoke of so many rules. My life ran along in a groove carved out by what I could and could not do. But now there are no rules. Only an attempt to figure out what actually makes sense in our lives when it comes to finding an ecological balance. But without the boundaries provided by the rules, I feel uprooted.

There is something so comforting about living within rules. On my blog, there are many hundreds of people now reporting that they have made eco-rules for their lives, too. My friend Rabbi Steve—referring to the rules of kosher—says that I have evolved a sort of "eco-Kashrut." Sometimes a group of rules and living traditions has the benefit of connecting you to some larger sense of community and meaning. Without the rules of No Impact, who am I?

There is that slice of pizza that so long ago I couldn't have and that I felt bitter about missing, but because it comes on a paper plate, I still can't bring myself to eat it. There is the taxicab that could get me from A to B without my getting wet in the rain, but it still pollutes the air and I can't bring myself to take it. I *do* take the elevator sometimes instead of the stairs, but I feel guilty.

I feel very lonely. Who could possibly understand the strangeness of the transition I am going through? I mean, it is more than just the project that has ended. It is my identity. My entire identity has disappeared. Yesterday, I was No Impact Man. What am I today? Moderate Impact Man?

What I'm describing sounds crazy, even to me, but as Annie Leonard says in her online video *Story of Stuff*, so is the norm:

> We are in this ridiculous situation where we go to work, maybe two jobs even, and we come home and we're exhausted so we plop down on our new couch and watch TV and the commercials tell us "YOU SUCK" so we gotta go to the mall to buy something to feel better, then we gotta go to work more to pay for the stuff we just bought so we come home and we're more tired so we sit down and watch more TV and it tells us to go to the mall again and we're on this crazy work-watch-spend treadmill. And we could just stop.

We could just stop.

Somewhere I read a talk of Pema Chödtrön's where she says something like, "Most of us in this room are not so rich that we have nothing material to worry about and we're not so poor that we can't think about anything but getting ourselves fed. So let's start by giving thanks for our middle birth."

What Pema means by "middle birth" is to be born neither in abject poverty nor in extreme wealth. We can be so overwhelmed by the suffering of poverty that we don't have the luxury to examine our lives. Or we can be so distant from suffering and so coddled by the material comforts of extreme wealth that we become too complacent to examine our lives. In a middle birth—where we are confronted with only moderate hardship—we have just enough suffering to get our attention but not enough to overwhelm us.

If the pleasures we seek are not permanent, then how important are they?

Perhaps part of the problem in our response to the planetary crisis—why we don't just stop, as Annie Leonard suggests—is that so many of us in the developed world have such a cushy lifestyle that we are stuck in our complacency.

This is like the story of the Buddha himself. His father, the king, wanted more than anything to protect his son from the knowledge of suffering. As a result, his son was never allowed to see anything that might upset him. Buddha came to believe that life was only about the pursuit of personal pleasure. He never questioned his life, because he never had a reason to. He just lived it as it had been delivered to him—until one day he ventured outside the palace.

For the first time he saw sick people and old people and dead bodies. He saw that these things ultimately happen to all of us. That sooner or later we all suffer. If old age and death are what happen to us, he asked, then what is the meaning of our lives? If the pleasures we seek are not permanent, then how important are they? What is the worth of all the riches and pleasures I've experienced in the palace if one day they will be taken away?

Buddha was shocked out of his complacency and began searching for a better life. The good news is that, at least as the legend goes, he found it.

Maybe this global-warming thing, along with all the environmental crises, along with the economic meltdown, could be for us in the developed world like leaving the palace and seeing the dead bodies and the old people and sick people. Maybe it will wake us up enough to ask: What is this life? What is it for? What is its meaning? How should we live?

Maybe it will wake us up enough to make us search for a better, more meaningful, more purposeful life—for us and for our planet.

Here's the big question I have about progress: If we can have better and better cell phones, but they are not accompanied by better and better understanding of ourselves and our place in this universe, can we really say that we have progressed? If we are born and then spend our lives moving from one toy to the next, without ever answering the big questions, have we progressed or have we simply been distracted?

Perhaps, if we really examined our lives, we'd come to the conclusion that our purpose is to make sure we can all ride around on Jet Skis during vacation and in SUVs the rest of the time. So be it. It's our life. It's our planet. As long as we make the collective decision consciously instead of blindly, then all well and good.

I suppose we could decide to burn hot and short. We could be the Hunter S. Thompson of species. I'm just suggesting that we should at least wake up long enough to make it an active decision. And, yes, it's our decision. It's a decision that belongs to us. Not to the government. Not to big business. It belongs to us.

If we do wake up, though, I rather doubt we'll decide to go out like Hunter Thompson. Mark Vonnegut, Kurt Vonnegut's son, went crazy and ended up in a mental hospital. Metaphorically speaking, he ventured outside the palace. He had to wake up. He had to ask himself some hard questions. This is why when his dad asked him what are we here for, Mark didn't say to ride on Jet Skis and in SUVs. Instead, he said, "We are here to help each other get through this thing, whatever it is." It was about helping each other.

I've had this hammered home to me lately—that if I want to manifest peace in the world, I have to find peace in my own mind.

They say a peaceful mind makes a peaceful man. A peaceful man makes a peaceful family. A peaceful family makes a peaceful village. A peaceful village makes a peaceful country. A peaceful country makes a peaceful world.

What does this mean? That if I want to change the world, I have to change myself.

There is a whole school of modern environmentalists, by the way, who don't much like connecting saving the planet with all this what's-the-meaning-of-life stuff to which I am so naturally inclined. They think it's a counterproductive turnoff that will have the effect of driving people away from, rather than toward, the idea of stewardship. They also worry—as I do—about tainting the environmental movement with thoughts of asceticism and having less.

They believe, as I do, that the human spirit is expansive and aspirational and that anything that reeks of tightening our belts or of being less or making ourselves smaller—part of the old environmentalism of the 1970s—is counter to human nature. They believe, as I do, in rising to the challenge rather than shrinking from the obstacles.

This group of modern environmentalists place its faith in technology—solar panels and electric cars and planet-saving inventions that no one has even heard of yet. New tech is cool and attractive to the young and fashionable and creates jobs for the underprivileged and deprived. More important, since the tighten-your-belt philosophy cannot apply to the bulk of human population, many of whom don't even have electricity, technology is the way to provide for the development of old and new economies in a sustainable way.

So these new, modern, gung-ho, "forward-looking" environmentalists are right. Aspiration and vision and a view to a better life, rather than a constricted life, is central. Technology is a hugely important part of the answer. But for a few reasons, I suspect it's not the whole answer.

For starters, to accomplish what is scientifically necessary to ameliorate catastrophic climate change, the United States would have to reduce its carbon emissions by at least 95 percent (some scientists are beginning to say 100 percent). In other words, we have to get the same result out of the same energy while causing twenty times less environmental damage. That's like telling the owner of an old juice factory that he needs to get the same juice from one orange that he used to get from twenty. He can get juicer oranges and he can get better juicing machines, but getting twenty oranges' worth of juice from one orange? Better tech may not be sufficient. We may also have to change the way we live.

Second, relying entirely on new tech may mean that we just create a whole new slew of environmental problems, like those created by the initial push for biofuels. The same thing applies if, for example, we choose to go with nuclear energy. What do we do with the waste?

Third, if we rely on technology alone, then we miss the tremendous opportunity for lifestyle improvement that we find in this crisis. If we build electric cars, we will still be stuck in traffic jams. If we keep building suburbs, we will still be isolated and lonely. If we put improving cell phones first, then our best minds will still be distracted from getting clean water to the billion who lack it. If we use technology, in other words, to rebuild the current system so that it can last forever, then we miss the opportunity to ask whether the current system really delivers the good life. We miss the opportunity to have happier people as well as a happier planet.

Working two jobs to get an electric car instead of the gas-guzzling variety is better, but it's still working two jobs. In an economy based on delivering the most stuff to the most people, education and health care are still secondary priorities. What if we redesigned our economy to include the cost of externalities like car exhaust and toxic garbage? What if we replaced GDP as our measure of national success with some measure of life quality? What if we designed our economy around the most important elements of the good life instead of around the throughput of material and energy? After all, if the environment and economic crises we currently face are any indicators, things the way they are aren't working.

What is the purpose of our lives?

What makes us happy and fulfilled?

The new environmentalists are right—we need to be expansive and aspirational. We also need huge investments in the rapid deployment of renewable energy production and sustainable technology. But conflating technology with progress is a two-hundred-year-old idea. It's not really aspirational. And it's not really progress. No, we need to figure out what the good life really is and then design our social and technical systems to facilitate it. Some people call this socio-technical design.

Which brings me back to the meaning-of-life questions. If we are to have good socio-technical design, we have to ask those questions. Why are we here? What is the purpose of our lives? What makes us happy and fulfilled? What, in short, is the good life? Because it is upon the definition of the good life that our socio-technical designs must be based.

Who, by the way, gets to decide what the good life is?

We do.

And who is *responsible* for deciding?

We are.

There has also been a debate raging within the environmental movement about the relative merits of individual versus collective action. Back in 2007, on the subject of individual action, the *New York Times* columnist Tom Friedman wrote, "You can change lights. You can change cars. But if you don't change leaders, your actions are nothing more than an expression of, as Dick Cheney would say, 'personal virtue.'"

Meanwhile, *Newsweek* reported that during the presidential campaign, Barack Obama remarked in frustration about having to answer a question by Brian Williams about his personal green choices: "What I'm thinking in my head is, 'Well, the truth is, Brian, we can't solve global warming because I f-----ing changed lightbulbs in my house. It's because of something collective.'"

I'd hear criticisms like this constantly throughout the No Impact project. What difference can one person make? Well, absolutely none if that one person doesn't try to make a difference. But who among us knows how much we will influence the people around us? Which one of us knows which of us, by applying their talents and efforts to what they believe in, may not become a Martin Luther King, Jr. or a Bobby Kennedy or a Betty Friedan or a Nelson Mandela?

Not that great names are necessarily the most important aspects of movements. They are like the proverbial straw that breaks the camel's back. Thousands and thousands of straws must weigh the camel down before the final one breaks its back. No one of these straws is more important than the other, not even the last one. It's just the one that happens to get remembered. Just because our individual actions are not remembered does not mean they're not crucial. The straw that breaks the back requires all of the rest of us straws. The domino that begins the domino effect requires each of us to be in line for the chain reaction to take place.

Of course, both Friedman and Obama are correct to suggest we need collective action on climate change. We need gigantic investment in green infrastructure. We need regulations to curb industry excesses. These things cannot be done by individuals. Those of us who are concerned about our environmental crisis must get involved in the political arena and find ways to keep pressure on our politicians in this regard.

But to suggest that collective and individual action are mutually exclusive, or even different, is wrongheaded and dangerous. It ignores the way cultures change, the responsibilities of citizens, and our potential as agents of change. Collective action is nothing more than the aggregation of individual actions. And individual action does not preclude involvement in collective action. In fact, it absolutely demands it. The two work together.

Think about this: How much more convincing is an advocate for urban bike lanes who rides his bike every day? Who is more convincing—an advocate for climate-change mitigation who takes the subway or one who drives alone in an SUV? Living our values across all areas of our individual lives—from the private to the public—demonstrates an integrity and conviction that can help persuade the skeptics. Instead of fruitlessly debating the utility of individual versus collective action, why not promote them both under an all-encompassing term like "engaged citizenship"?

The climate crisis has revealed a second crisis: the inability of our culture to effect rapid and crucial change. Through what channels do we exercise our concern to get something done about the climate crisis? The federal government has a record of making itself too cumbersome and too beholden to institutional interests to lead radical change. It tends to yoyo between more tax and more government and less tax and less government. Back and forth. It is not good at leading larger cultural change.

The climate problem is so big that we need a change in the culture. We need to look at the way we live. We need to find a good life that does not depend so much on energy and material throughput. And government should not be in the business of telling us how to live. Government should be in the business of facilitating the way of life the people have chosen. If we want to ensure that the planet maintains its ability to support us, we have to choose differently. This is a battle not just for votes but for hearts and minds. And hearts and minds are captured by individuals, not by governments.

We know we have to change the system, but we must also remember that the system is only a collection of individuals. What the system does is just the aggregation of all of our individual actions as citizens, as shareholders, as CEOs, as product designers, as customers, as friends, as family members, and as voters. We have to stop waiting for the system to change and remember that every decision we make in our homes and in our workplaces amounts to "the system."

On the street, people tell jokes. They say excuse me if they bump into each other. They help each other. But we go to work and make decisions that are "not personal but business." Our institutions don't reflect our human kindness. We allow our corporations to focus only on profits. We allow political institutions to focus mostly on reelection. We must insist that our institutions reflect the full truth of the humanity they are supposed

We cannot wait for the system to change.
We individuals are the system.

to serve. We must, in our roles within those institutions, act the same way we would act when we find an old person having trouble crossing the street.

As individuals—as product designers and accountants and CEOs, for example—we all make crucial decisions that affect the world. We cannot wait for the system to change. We individuals are the system.

We need to pick up a new model of engaged citizenship and realize that the way we live affects everyone around us. We need to develop new ways to take up and assert our responsibility. We need to take "participatory democracy" to a new level, where we don't just vote for the leaders who will bring us the culture we want, but where we take responsibility for making the culture ourselves.

And what we get in return is the feeling of a life fully lived, in a world where we are not victims of the system but leaders of it. Where we choose instead of inherit. Where we stride purposefully instead of sleepwalk. Where we are true masters of our destiny. So. About these questions regarding what I did about toilet paper and what parts of the project I kept:

I was in a radio studio in midtown Manhattan doing a live interview with a presenter from the BBC World Service. He asked me about the toilet paper. By then, I had been asked about this by journalists from Montreal to Tel Aviv, and I was sick of it. I would always deflect the question by saying that this was no trivial issue.

Why, when the world is in peril, would you waste all of our time discussing my toilet habits? I would say. How crazy is it, I would ask, that we chop down the trees we need to absorb carbon dioxide and then flush them down our toilets? There are better systems, I would say.

But this one particular BBC journalist would not let it go. "Yes," he said, "but our listeners would like to know what you did instead of toilet paper."

Finally, I snapped. I said, "I clearly do not want to discuss my toilet habits on the radio, and I'm sure your listeners are embarrassed for you that you keep pressing me on this issue. Would your mother be proud of you for asking such a personal and embarrassing question within the hearing of millions? Because I'm sure my mother would not be proud of me for answering you."

That put it to bed.

As for what we kept, well, let me say first that I am over the strange confusion and shame that infected me in the first week.

The refrigerator is back on but the freezer, which is separate, is not. After a year of disuse, the dishwasher would not come back to life, and we did not replace it. We gave our air conditioners away and sweated through the summer and plan to keep doing so. The radiators are still turned off. There is no TV, though we park Isabella in front of a movie on the computer once in a while. I carry my jar everywhere for coffee and water and, mostly, ride my bike. I have been in perhaps ten taxis in the year since the project ended, and I take the subway when it rains.

I still wash my hair with baking soda, and use it for deodorant. I use homemade moisturizer and soap with no toxins. We still don't eat meat. Sadly, for me, Isabella, who is now three and half, got angry and said she did not want to be a vegetarian anymore. She said the other kids get to eat meat and she wants to, too.

"Do you know that meat is animals?" I asked.

"Yes."

"So if you eat meat, you're eating animals. You get it?"

"Yes, I want to eat animals," Isabella said.

So this Thanksgiving, Michelle and I decided that she could have turkey at her friend Ruby's house. The turkey came, Isabella tasted it, but she didn't like it. She asked for cheese.

As for those questions I'm still left with after the No Impact experiment, let's start with this one: How do we save the world? How do we keep ourselves from going extinct? I say this starkly, because if you read the scientific literature, you'll find this climate emergency is much worse than the press is making out.

The answer to my question is that I don't think anybody fully knows yet. This is why it is not a problem that can be outsourced to government alone. We all have to turn our minds to it. But before we turn our minds to it, we have to actually believe we can make a difference. That, by the way, is one of the most important results of the project: that I've come to believe that I can make a difference.

Paradoxically, it may not have been the creating less trash and other measures per se that made the greatest difference. Instead, what made the difference was publicly letting people know that I was trying, and trying hard, and having them see the efforts. Going to extremes for a year changed the way I think about these things—another result of the experiment. Changing the people around me—the unforeseen consequence of individual action—is still one more result. By continuing to think about these issues and doing my best, even if it's not as extreme as during the project proper, I continue to change the people around me. We can all change the people around us by changing ourselves.

I still sometimes flounder. I'm far from perfect. I'm cruel sometimes and insensitive. I get all caught up in my petty concerns. Indeed, people close to me have called me a hypocrite at times for my callousness. "How can you call yourself No Impact Man?" they've said. They're right, of course.

But what wouldn't be right is if I didn't at least in some small way keep trying to do something.

I can choose how I live. I can be involved politically. I can give talks and try to change other people's minds. I can participate in the local community garden and see if the idea of urban agriculture catches fire. I can carry my jar around. I can take planes less. I can blog. I can talk to people. I can look for new ways to participate in our cultural response to our environmental crises.

I'm not going to make myself a martyr. But I am going to keep trying to live my life deliberately. For most of my forty-five years I didn't try hard enough. I got too paralyzed by this question of whether I was the type of person who could make a difference. Finally, during the year of the project, I realized that's the wrong question. The real question is whether I'm the type of person who wants to try.

Throughout this book I've tried to show how saving the world is up to me. I've tried hard not to lecture. Yes, it's up to me. But after living for a year without toilet paper, I've earned the right to say one thing: It's also up to you.

So, what are you going to do?

Explore

Visit Colin Beavan's *No Impact Man* blog (http://noimpactman.typepad.com/blog/) and read up on the details of his yearlong experiment. What were the rules of his no impact experiment? Do you think you could incorporate any of his practices into your own daily routine? How does Beavan link his environmentally friendly practices to self fulfillment? What do you think is the significance of his making this connection?

Collaborate

After familiarizing yourself with the *No Impact Man* experiment via Beavan's blog (see above), book, or film, choose one or two of his no impact rules to follow as a class for one week. Create a blog that documents this experiment, noting both failures and successes. In composing your collaborative blog, keep in mind that you can use both descriptive writing and photographic images to document your experience.

Compose

Read the excerpt from the graphic novel *As the World Burns: 50 Simple Things You Can Do to Stay in Denial,* on page 117. Write an essay in which you describe how this text seems to respond to Beavan's project. What criticisms does it seem to level and why? Having read both texts, which approach to environmental activism do you think more compelling or effective?

Mike Tidwell, executive director of the Chesapeake Climate Action Network, wrote this column for the December 6, 2009, edition of The Washington Post. *The meeting in Copenhagen to which Tidwell refers was the United Nations-sponsored climate conference designed to address global warming.*

TO REALLY SAVE THE PLANET, STOP GOING GREEN

BY MIKE TIDWELL

As President Obama heads to Copenhagen next week for global warming talks, there's one simple step Americans back home can take to help out: Stop "going green." Just stop it. No more compact fluorescent light bulbs. No more green wedding planning. No more organic toothpicks for holiday hors d'oeuvres.

December should be national Green-Free Month. Instead of continuing our faddish and counterproductive emphasis on small, voluntary actions, we should follow the example of Americans during past moral crises and work toward large-scale change. The country's last real moral and social revolution was set in motion by the civil rights movement. And in the 1960s, civil rights activists didn't ask bigoted Southern governors and sheriffs to consider "10 Ways to Go Integrated" at their convenience.

Green gestures we have in abundance in America. Green political action, not so much. And the gestures ("Look honey, another *Vanity Fair* Green Issue!") lure us into believing that broad change is happening when the data shows that it isn't. Despite all our talk about washing clothes in cold water, we aren't making much of a difference.

For eight years, George W. Bush promoted voluntary action as the nation's primary response to global warming—and for eight years, aggregate greenhouse gas emissions remained unchanged. Even today, only 10 percent of our household light bulbs are compact fluorescents. Hybrids account for only 2.5 percent of U.S. auto sales. One can almost imagine the big energy companies secretly applauding each time we distract ourselves from the big picture with a hectoring list of "5 Easy Ways to Green Your Office."

As America joins the rest of the world in finally fighting global warming, we need to bring our battle plan up to scale. If you believe that astronauts have been to the moon and that the world is not flat, then you probably believe the satellite photos showing the Greenland ice sheet in full-on meltdown. Much of Manhattan and the Eastern Shore of Maryland may join the Atlantic Ocean in our lifetimes. Entire Pacific island nations will disappear. Hurricanes will bring untold destruction. Rising sea levels and crippling droughts will decimate crops and cause widespread famine. People will go hungry, and people will die.

Morally, this is sort of a big deal. It would be wrong to let all this happen when we have the power to prevent the worst of it by adopting clean-energy policies.

But how do we do that? Again, look to the history of the civil rights struggle. After many decades of public denial and inaction, the civil rights movement helped Americans to see Southern apartheid in moral terms. From there, the movement succeeded by working toward legal change. Segregation was phased out rapidly only because it was phased out through the law. These statutes didn't erase racial prejudice from every American heart overnight. But through them, our country made staggering progress. Just consider who occupies the White House today.

All who appreciate the enormity of the climate crisis still have a responsibility to make every change possible in their personal lives. I have, from the solar panels on my roof to the Prius in my driveway to my low-carbon-footprint vegetarian diet. But surveys show that very few people are willing to make significant voluntary changes, and those of us who do create the false impression of mass progress as the media hypes our actions.

Instead, most people want carbon reductions to be mandated by laws that will allow us to share both the responsibilities and the benefits of change. Ours is a nation of laws; if we want to alter our practices in a deep and lasting way, this is where we must start. After years of delay and denial and green half-measures, we must legislate a stop to the burning of coal, oil and natural gas.

Of course, all this will require congressional action, and therein lies the source of Obama's Copenhagen headache. To have been in the strongest position to negotiate a binding emissions treaty with other world leaders this month, the president needed a strong carbon-cap bill out of Congress. But the House of Representatives passed only a weak bill riddled with loopholes in June, and the Senate has failed to get even that far.

So what's the problem? There's lots of blame to go around, but the distraction of the "go green" movement has played a significant role. Taking their cues from the popular media and cautious politicians, many Americans have come to believe that they are personally to blame for global warming and that they must fix it, one by one, at home. And so they either do as they're told—a little of this, a little of that—or they feel overwhelmed and do nothing.

We all got into this mess together. And now, with treaty talks underway internationally and Congress stalled at home, we need to act accordingly. Don't spend an hour changing your light bulbs. Don't take a day to caulk your windows. Instead, pick up a phone, open a laptop, or travel to a U.S. Senate office near you and turn the tables: "What are the 10 green statutes you're working on to save the planet, Senator?"

Demand a carbon-cap bill that mandates the number 350. That's the level of carbon pollution scientists say we must limit ourselves to: 350 parts per million of CO_2 in the air. If we can stabilize the atmosphere at that number in coming decades, we should be able to avoid the worst-case scenario and preserve a planet similar to the one human civilization developed on. To get there, America will need to make deep but achievable pollution cuts well before 2020. And to protect against energy price shocks during this transition, Congress must include a system of direct rebates to consumers, paid for by auctioning permit fees to the dirty-energy companies that continue to pollute our sky.

Obama, too, needs to step up his efforts; it's not just Congress and the voters who have been misguided. Those close to the president say he understands the seriousness of global warming. But despite the issue's moral gravity, he's been paralyzed by political caution. He leads from the rear on climate change, not from the front.

Forty-five years ago, President Lyndon B. Johnson faced tremendous opposition on civil rights from a Congress dominated by Southern leaders, yet he spent the political capital necessary to answer a great moral calling. Whenever key bills on housing, voting and employment stalled, he gave individual members of congress the famous "Johnson treatment." He charmed. He pleaded. He threatened. He led, in other words, in person, and from the front.

Does anyone doubt that our charismatic current president has the capacity to turn up the heat? Imagine the back-room power of a full-on "Obama treatment" to defend America's flooding coastlines and burning Western forests. Imagine a two-pronged attack on the fickle, slow-moving Senate: Obama on one side and a tide of tweets and letters from voters like you.

So join me: Put off the attic insulation job till January. Stop searching online for recycled gift wrapping paper and sustainably farmed Christmas trees. Go beyond green fads for a month, and instead help make green history.

According to Tidwell, American citizens should demand a carbon-cap bill that mandates 350 parts per million of CO_2 in the air. Use your library to research the rationale behind a carbon-cap bill. What is it, and how would it work? Do you think this is a viable proposal for preventing climate change?

According to Tidwell, the movement to personally "go green" has distracted American citizens and political leaders from taking real political action to prevent climate change. How does this claim undermine the lifestyle choices espoused by Beavan (page 99) and Matheson (page 83)? Write a response paper in which you describe the crucial differences between these authors. Which approach (personal or legislative) do you think is the most crucial to preventing further environmental damage? Is there a way to reconcile these opposed positions?

Tidwell argues that we should urge our representatives to pass laws that would protect the environment. Follow Tidwell's advice and write a letter to your senators or representatives asking them to sponsor a particular statute that would help the environment.

Activists Derrick Jensen and Stephanie McMillan teamed to produce the graphic novel As the World Burns: 50 Simple Things You Can Do to Stay in Denial *in 2007. Jensen has written several books and in 2008 was named one of* Utne Reader's *"50 Visionaries Who Are Changing Your World." McMillan began syndicating her political cartoons in 1999, and a book based on her comic strip "Minimum Security" was published in 2005. Seven Stories Press, which published* As the World Burns, *offers this description of the book on its website: "Two of America's most talented activists team up to deliver a bold and hilarious satire of modern environmental policy in this fully illustrated graphic novel. The U.S. government gives robot machines from space permission to eat the earth in exchange for bricks of gold. A one-eyed bunny rescues his friends from a corporate animal-testing laboratory. And two little girls figure out the secret to saving the world from both of its enemies (and it isn't by using energy-efficient light bulbs or biodiesel fuel).* As the World Burns *will inspire you to do whatever it takes to stop ecocide before it's too late." Jensen and McMillan continue to create and publish an* As the World Burns *serial graphic novel online at http://sevenstories.com/astheworldburns.*

excerpt from

AS THE WORLD BURNS: 50 SIMPLE THINGS YOU CAN DO TO STAY IN DENIAL

BY DERRICK JENSEN AND STEPHANIE MCMILLAN

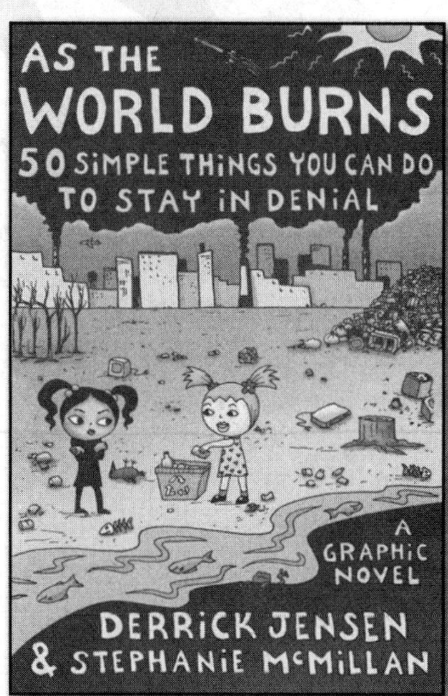

You mean big industries can make lots of money by building dams for aluminum smelting, choking the life out of rivers and killing the fish, plus tearing up great swaths of Africa for mining bauxite?

WOW!

Big money for builders, miners and manufacturers!

Then countless people can acquire Alzheimer's Disease from ingesting the toxic metal!

Drinking the soda from the cans will help millions enjoy diabetes, obesity and malnutrition!

And then they'll add the cans to millions of other used cans and melt them down using coal-burning plants that spew toxins into the air,
and then use all that metal to make more cans, using still more energy.

So you can drink more soda.

And the melting and re-forming will take somewhat less energy than making all totally new cans.
So as a FABULOUS BONUS...

You can watch three episodes of "Survivor," or even six "Brady Bunch" reruns with the energy that's saved.
Therefore using the same amount of energy as before, but gaining three hours of brainwashing! What a brilliant scheme!

You're a real party-pooper, you know that?

Wouldn't it be wonderful if life were this simple, the problems we face so easily solvable? Every cell in my body wants for recycling to save the day, wants for shorter showers to save enough water for the rivers to run free.

But they won't. You know that. Fish and turtles and beavers and frogs and bears know that. Everybody knows that.

Sometimes we forget.

I just saw a great movie about how the world is heating up, and about what we can do to stop it.
Finally the issue is being addressed? It's about damn time.
One thing we can do is to change our light bulbs.
Light bulbs.
Light bulbs?
Replacing one regular light bulb with a compact flourescent saves 150 pounds of carbon dioxide per year!
That's their solution?!
Oh, there's so much more!
I can hardly wait.

Oooh, fox-ay!

There's a layer of reality not perceived by our five senses, that connects us to everything.
You only have five?

What we're experiencing is a result of what's going on within ourselves.
We're the solution, as well as the problem, as well as the creators of the problem.
Meditation is key. The infinite source of all reality will solve the Earth's dilemma.

This will change the world.
I invite you to try it with me.

Before me peaceful.
Behind me peaceful.
Above me peaceful.
Below me ...

Ready to stop global warming?

I'm so excited!

Yeah, let's stop the burning of oil and coal!

Me too! All we need to do is dismantle the industrial economy!

So... we already talked about changing light bulbs.

You think I'm kidding.

Don't be Silly.

The movie said we should drive less. Walk, bike, carpool or take mass transit more often. You'll save one pound of carbon dioxide for every mile you don't drive.

Which means you put out one pound for every mile you do...

Just stop it. Stop it. Stop it. Let me continue.
Okay.
You don't like my list.

Your list is fine.
It's just.... just...

Just go on. Please.

Okay! You're really going to like this one! It's really important, and you don't have to change your lifestyle at all!
Well, thank goodness for that!

Check your tires: keeping your tires inflated properly can improve gas mileage by more than 3%. Every gallon of gasoline saved keeps 20 pounds of carbon dioxide out of the atmosphere.

Which means that every gallon burned...

Why do you do this?

What?

Ruin everything. That's all you do.

Please, go on.

Use less hot water.

Will that stop global warming?

Oh yes! It takes a lot of energy to heat water.

You can install a low flow showerhead to save 350 pounds of CO_2 per year, and wash your clothes in cold or warm water to save 500 pounds per year.

Another important one is to avoid products with a lot of packaging.
I can still buy things, right? I just avoid the ones with packaging...

That's it exactly! You can save 1,200 pounds of carbon dioxide if you cut down your garbage by 10 percent!

The next one is to adjust your thermostat. Moving your thermostat down just two degrees in winter and up two degrees in summer could save about 2,000 pounds of CO_2 a year.

Oh, and you'll love this one, since you love nature. Plant a tree!!
A single tree will absorb one ton of CO2 during its lifetime.
How about if we stop someone from cutting down a tree?
I suppose that would work. But wouldn't it be hard?
I'd just rather plant a little tree all my own and watch it grow and grow and grow.
Wouldn't that be fun?

we will go quietly, meekly, to the end of the world, if only you allow us to believe that buying low energy light bulbs will save us.

I did some math with that global warming list.
Let's pretend everybody in the United States does everything on that list.
Wouldn't that be wonderful?
And let's pretend they change not one light bulb but every light bulb in their homes.
That would make me so happy!
You and the light bulb manufacturers both.
That would save about 400 million tons of carbon dioxide.
Yippee!! I told you this would save the world!
And that's only one item on the list!
Next, people in the United States drive about 2.3 trillion miles per year.
If we cut that in half we save about 575 million tons of carbon dioxide.
You do like my list! Oh, you do, you do!

Recycling half of every American's household waste would save about 125 million tons.
Inflating tires and thus increasing gas mileage would save about 85 million tons.
Inflate the tires, yes!
Low flow showerheads and washing clothes in cooler water would save 105 million tons.
I could do that! So could everyone else!
Cutting down on garbage by ten percent reduces emissions by 65 million tons.
And I don't even mind that we counted that one twice! We have so much to spare!
Adjusting the thermostat will save about 105 million tons.
Lowering it two degrees in the summer might be hard. It's so hot out! But to save the world I would do that, wouldn't you?
If every person in the United States planted a tree, that would absorb seven million tons of carbon dioxide a year.
I can add it all up! It makes a total of about 1.5 billion tons of carbon dioxide a year!

We did it! We saved the planet!

That's if every person in the United States does every one of these things.
But they will! If we just tell them. This isn't so hard! We can do it!

There's just one thing. Total carbon emissions for the United States is 7.1 billion tons.
If every man, woman and child did all of the things on the list from the movie ~ and you know there is precisely zero chance that every man, woman and child in the United States will do this...

I don't like where this is going

That would only be about a 21 percent reduction in carbon emissions. And since total carbon emissions go up about two percent per year, that whole reduction would disappear in about...

* sigh. *

Using your library's resources or the web, research the definitional criteria for satire. (What is a satire? What are the essential criteria of the genre?) Based on these criteria, do you think this excerpt from *As the World Burns* qualifies as a satire? How so? Do you think the text is effective?

Look closely at the hand-drawn images in *As the World Burns*. What do you notice about the style of the drawings? How are the humans characterized? The animals? How does the artist represent big corporations? What messages about human impact on the environment (and about environmentalism itself) do these images seem to convey?

As the World Burns uses a combination of images and texts to make a claim about the human impact on the environment and about our attempts to repair what damage we've done. With some of the strategies of the graphic novel in mind, compose a multi-modal essay in which you use images and text in combination to make a claim about an environmental issue. Have a specific claim in mind and seek out (or take) photographs that, when read in a careful progression, help articulate your argument. Carefully write and pair short captions for each image and put them into a narrative form.

Anne Marie Todd is an associate professor of communication studies at San Jose State University. Her essay "Prime Time Subversion" was published in the 2002 collection Enviropop: Studies in Environmental Rhetoric and Popular Culture.

PRIME-TIME SUBVERSION: THE ENVIRONMENTAL RHETORIC OF THE SIMPSONS

BY ANNE MARIE TODD

On April 19, 1987, America was introduced to the Simpsons, the title family of the first animated prime-time television series since the 1960s. Described by its creator and executive producer Matt Groening as "a celebration of the American family at its wildest" (Steiger, 1999, p. 1), *The Simpsons* offered a critical view of mainstream social and cultural norms. In a television world dominated by upper-middle-class storybook families like the Huxtables of *The Cosby Show*, *The Simpsons* presented a satirical documentary of a more complex family whose characters and plots related more directly to the familial experience of America's television audience. In fact, *The Simpsons* first aired on prime-time television opposite *The Cosby Show*, assuming a revolutionary position toward mainstream television and the network establishment. The series exhibited a realism that appealed to a widely diverse audience and established *The Simpsons* as a fixture of American prime-time. When the show debuted, it quickly became the FOX Network's highest rated program (Korte, 1997, p.1). The success of *The Simpsons* is evident in the show's impressive popularity with a heterogeneous audience that spans generations. The program has also won critical acclaim, and has received numerous awards, including the Peabody Award (1997), the People's Choice Award (1990-1991) and several Emmies (Steiger, 1999, p.2). As Steiger argued, *The Simpsons'* "vicious social satire" and subtle profound "pop-culture allusions" had a "considerable impact on the television landscape of the nation" (p. 2).

Multiple layers of profound social and cultural commentary distinguish *The Simpsons* from conventional television programs. "The critical humor, self-reflexiveness, intertextuality and form" of *The Simpsons* solidify the literary significance of the series' postmodern commentary (Korte, 1997, p. 3). Such rhetorical elements help establish the Simpson family as an icon of American popular culture. In 1998, *Time* magazine listed Bart Simpson on behalf of the entire series as one of the key cultural and most influential figures of the twentieth century (Steiger, 1999, p.2). The realism of the characters and plot lines of *The Simpsons* give the series a dramatic quality; the Simpsons' family adventures expose the nuances of American family life while simultaneously informing the social and cultural experience of the television audience.

Critical and popular acclaim for *The Simpsons* distinguishes the series as a rich multi-dimensional text for rhetorical analysis. In countless interviews, Matt Groening has described *The Simpsons* as a show that rewards its audience for paying attention (Korte, 1997, p. 9). As the most counter-cultural cartoon to hit prime-time, the series is ripe for rhetorical inquiry into its potential as a vehicle for critical political and social commentary. *The Simpsons* contributes significantly to critical analysis of popular culture, particularly in the study of television media, because the show is more literary and complex than regular television programming (Korte, 1997, p. 7). In a decade, *The Simpsons* has secured immense popularity, and its established prime-time slot confirms the magnitude of the show's viewing audience. With its copious literary and cinematic references and interminable political commentary, *The Simpsons* is indisputably embedded in American culture, and thus offers a lens into the rhetorical dimensions of human experience. Rhetorical analysis of popular culture is indispensable in the exposition of the social, cultural, and political motivations of human action. Our understanding of meaning and our comprehension of rhetorical symbols are best achieved through the explication of human motives. Rhetorical analysis of popular culture discloses how communication of symbols in the interpretation of personal experience promotes a persuasive rhetoric that engenders critical commentary regarding the social and cultural dimensions of human experience.

This chapter explicates the meaning and significance of *The Simpsons'* social commentary through two mediums of rhetorical criticism. The first method of analysis utilizes Kenneth Burke's (1959) comic frame to determine the meaning of the show's multi-textual rhetoric. Analysis of televisual communication requires an enhanced application of the comic form through a second mode of inquiry, the explication of the symbolism of *The Simpsons'* visual argument. The show presents a unique rhetorical form that exhibits profound pop-cultural influence, and in particular makes a significant impression on American environmental consciousness. This analysis begins with an explication of the utility of the comic frame and visual argument as prolific tools of rhetorical criticism. The synthesis of these two approaches engenders an enriched analysis, which articulates *The Simpsons'* intertextual environmental rhetoric. Next, the convergence of comic and visual critical practices is examined, which illuminates the symbolic elements of the show's environmental rhetoric. The abundance of episodic material, teeming with rich dialogue and resplendent visuals, rendered focusing this analysis an enigmatic task. As a directive for this criticism, two predominant metaphors are explored: Springfield's nuclear power plant as an icon of irresponsible energy use and the figurative role of nonhuman characters in the series. This project's conclusion articulates the coherent ecological message in *The Simpsons'* rhetoric, and thus renders a conclusive evaluation of the show's televisual environmental commentary. Specifically, I propose that the show's rhetoric presents a strong environmental message regarding the relationship between humans and the rest of nature.

This message is most clearly articulated in the show's rhetorical strategies, which reveal a pervasive ecological criticism of human activity, produced through comedy and visual argument—rhetorical tools that successfully engage the audience in *The Simpsons'* critical environmental commentary. This rhetorical criticism examines the first ten seasons of the series in recognition of the rhetorical force with which these animated social texts exhibit the interface of environmental communication and popular culture. The analysis was conducted by viewing various collected videotapes of the series' first ten seasons (4/9/87-5/16/99)—approximately 80 percent of the episodes—and supplemented with data from Matt Groening's two-volume guide to the show. The ten years of episodes in the sample provide hundreds of rhetorical propositions of ecological tone. Conducting a satisfactory analysis of all such references in the confines of this chapter is impossible. Thus, I focused primarily (almost exclusively) on the show's principal environmental symbols and themes. As a result, the discussion focuses on only a few entire episodes, significant plot lines, familiar environmental theses, and explicit recurring rhetorical symbols. By focusing on the dominant characteristics of *The Simpsons'* environmental communication, I endeavored to limit the scope of criticism, and thus foster a more informed evaluation of the overall environmental message of the show. Ultimately, these televised visual and linguistic images disclose the show itself as an expression of environmental activism, and expose the salience of *The Simpsons*' environmental rhetoric.

THE COMIC FRAME: TRANSCENDING THE SOCIAL ORDER THROUGH SYMBOLIC ACTION

In *A Rhetoric of Motives* (1950), Kenneth Burke describes the study of rhetoric as the understanding of human motives, and his theory of symbolic action provides the basis for innumerable conceptions of the study of rhetoric. Contextualizing the comic frame within a theory of rhetoric as symbolic action, Arne Madsen cites Burke's definition of humans as symbol-using creatures that construct responses to everyday experiences. That is, human action involves using and manipulating symbols to respond to interpretations of experience (Madsen, 1993, p. 166). In this way, rhetorical criticism relies on the explication of symbols to understand human responses to experience. The rhetorical critic must analyze such behavior in order to understand human motives and to comprehend how the manipulation of symbols influences human behavior. Burke expounds on this concept of symbolic rhetoric as an explanation for human motivation in *Language as Symbolic Action* (1966). He argues that human communication involves the expression of symbolic meaning in order to directly influence the behavior and conduct of one's audience (Burke, 1966, p. 28). That is, we use symbols to construct arguments, and conceptually plan courses of action based on our interpretation of our experience.

This discussion of the symbolic expression of motives provides a context for Burke's presentation of the comic frame in *Attitudes Toward History* (1959). He introduces the comic frame as a means to enhance scholars' understanding of human motivations and foster better evaluation of the social and cultural meaning of symbolic action. The comic frame enables individuals to "be observers of themselves, while acting [to create] maximum consciousness. One would 'transcend himself by noting his own foibles" (Burke, 1959, p. 171). Burke envisioned that applying the comic frame would create social consciousness to expose the impotence of the status quo—the existing social order—and create public awareness to address the failings of the social system. The comic frame fosters more than an ironic self-awareness, but also constructs a position of semi-detachment, where one is able to reflect and comment on human foibles without guilt, shame, or other negative emotion, or without undue involvement in the human comedy. Toward this end, Burke established the utility of frames as tools for rhetorical criticism; he described frames as the perspectives that

direct all interpretations of human experience. That is, frames provide symbolic structure that enables human beings to impose order upon their personal and social experiences. Rhetorical criticism involves the dual-purposed application of frames to episodes of human experience—frames function as blueprints for actions that fix social attitudes according to a particular perspective. Frames also embody attitudes and motives, empowering scholars to determine various social and cultural forms of symbolic action (Burke, 1959, p. 20). In this way, the comic frame enriches rhetorical criticism by revealing the flaws of the present system, enabling alternative discourse to gain public recognition.

Comedy provides the means to criticize one's own complicity in the dominant social order. By acknowledging the failings of the bureaucratic system, humans create discursive space for self-analysis. Such personal criticism involves a discourse that promotes historically marginalized opinions within the public sphere. Thus, the comic frame is rhetorically powerful on two levels: through recognition of human error as the cause of social ills, and through the spiritual and moral identification with humanity. By creating social distance between reformers and the clown as a scapegoat, the comic frame also conveys a preference for a social upbraiding, rather than malicious immolation, to promote the rapprochement engendered by comic consciousness. *The Simpsons* utilizes the comic frame to identify the incongruity of human action and the symbolic interpretation of the ecological context of our experience.

POPULAR CULTURE IMAGERY AS SOCIAL COMMENTARY: THE RHETORIC OF VISUAL ARGUMENT

The coherence of the environmental message of *The Simpsons* is enriched by the show's televisual rhetorical form. The series' animated realism informs traditional methods of rhetorical criticism by illuminating tactics of visual argument. Contemporary rhetorical theory, guided by Susanne Langer, Kenneth Burke, Ernest Bormann and others, emphasizes the symbolic form of rhetorical discourse (Klumpp & Hollihan, 1989, p. 88). Accordingly, the persuasive force of rhetoric is rooted in the motivational power of symbol, located in the relationship between rhetoric and the reality of the social order. The rhetorical critic's objective is to illuminate and evaluate persuasive messages (Andrews, 1990, p. 14) and thus determine the ways in which rhetorical discourse functions as symbolic action in response to different rhetorical situations. Rhetorical criticism is concerned with the persuasiveness of discourse through the "creation of social forms in human symbolic behavior" (Klumpp & Hollihan,

1989, p. 88). That is, the salience of rhetorical propositions is largely based on the correspondence of the symbolic value of a discourse with the established meaning of the existing social order. Stating the case for visual communication, Blair (1996) argues that "the concept of visual argument is an extension of rhetoric's paradigm into a new domain...[R]hetoric in a broader sense is the use of symbols to communicate...[A]ny form of persuasion, including visual persuasion, belongs within rhetoric's province" (p. 37). With the emergence of visual communication as an acknowledged persuasive force, rhetorical critics must identify ways to evaluate the meaning of visual arguments.

Contemporary analysis of the social and cultural context of human communication must account for the increased mediation of rhetorical messages. Analysis of televised communication acts requires amplified discursive frames to evaluate the complex argumentation strategies fostered by expanded media formats. Television media enjoy a substantially larger audience than traditional rhetorical settings, and thus must account for the diverse experiences of television viewers. In addition, televised messages are informed by the broader context of rhetorical symbols and are thus enabled to offer critical commentary on the social, cultural, and political experience of the American viewing public. Gronbeck (1995) offers a defense of visual argument, and argues that rhetorical meaning requires interpretation to decode the symbols of a message. He posits that symbolic meaning is not exclusively linguistic, and visual, aural, and other symbolic systems can offer propositions that affirm or deny social and cultural experience (p. 539).

Visual media are capable of symbolic expression because they are rooted in a particularly rich context of social, cultural and political influences. The complexities of the existing social order are manifest in the stream of televised visual images—elemental, socio-cultural interpretations of human experience. Effective visual communication exhibits rich and visual symbolism that incorporates signs and symbols of conventionalized images (Blair, 1996, p. 25). The symbolic form of visual argument is deeply rooted in the context of pop culture, a rubric for the innumerable vernacular of consumer cultural images. For this reason, visual arguments enjoy an appeal that eludes verbal communication: ocular recognition of pictorial images evokes meaning that is rooted in the memory of personal experience. Visual messages persuade because they provoke "unconscious identification," which are not possible with the linguistic basis of verbal images (Blair, 1996, p. 34). Thus, visual images persuade because they give meaning to personal experience by connecting thematic elements of shared social experience (whether televised experience or actual, real experience) to individual perception. Audience members incorporate the symbolic meaning of the visual image(s) into their personal value system, affecting their individual and social worldviews (Blair, 1996, p. 34). The symbolism of visual images remains ambiguous without a stabilizing linguistic text. Thus, the rhetorical force of one visual image appeals to a heterogeneous audience because pictorial symbols adapt to individualized experience, and encompass many meanings.

Visual argument is gaining particular ascendance as a rhetorical device with the technological improvement of visual communication, notably the advent of digital technology and the remarkable realism of computer animation. A rhetoric of visual discourse employs aesthetic symbols to inform social action. Visual tactics of communication rely on personal allegiances and affinities, which evoke dramatic reactions based on the rhetorical force of the visual image. Individual interpretation entails the personal association of familiar visual images within a normalizing social context. Such personal interpretation makes individual actions meaningful because the actions are grounded in a social context, and the social context in turn guides individual behavior according to established social and cultural norms. Visual argument facilitates social change by compelling individuals to modify their behavior to accommodate the symbolic norms of visual discourse. Visual images resonate with personal experience, facilitating the production of social meaning. Furthermore, visual argument enjoys an element of realism that makes its interpretation of human experience uniquely persuasive to individuals who can understand the context of the rhetorical message.

The Simpsons is an animated cartoon rather than a show filmed with real actors in an actual physical setting. The animation creates an air of detachment from real life, in addition to the detachment created by the comic frame. Animation is a particularly salient medium to television viewers who can suspend belief for plot development (which they would not be able to do with real characters). At the same time, the show establishes a personal connection with viewers because the characters are believable.

Television programming is provocative because it engages the audience through the mediation of social situations, which imparts socially constructed norms under the guise of actual experiential knowledge. Television, particularly animation, misrepresents reality, masquerading as lived experience, in order to manipulate social contexts that provide meaning for personal experience, and guide individual action.

THE ENVIRONMENTAL POLITICS OF THE SPRINGFIELD NUCLEAR POWER PLANT

"Both overshadowing and enlightening" (Steiger, 1999, p. 4), Springfield's nuclear power plant is owned and operated by the miserly Montgomery Burns, the town's wealthiest citizen. Homer is an employee of the plant, and holds the title of safety inspector despite his egregious lack of training. A Springfield institution, the plant is prominently featured in the show as a visual scenic element or as a comedic factor in plot development. The plant's prominence as a visual symbol of the show's environmental message is exhibited in the longer version of the show's opening sequence. The camera moves in over a hillside for a view of the picturesque town, marred only by the centrally positioned image of the plant's twin smokestacks, which billow thick clouds of dark gray smoke. The rampant pollution billowing from the smokestacks juxtaposed to the unsullied town landscape is a disturbing image. This disturbing introduction exemplifies the show's dark humor, and the potent combination of visual argument and comic frame. The negative symbolic image of the plant's egregious emissions, the dark gray billowing smoke, is reinforced by its contrast with the depiction of the town, which is animated in unrealistically bright colors. The plant symbolizes the show's environmental commentary by exhibiting a wide range of ecological implications of nuclear power, in general, and of specific conditions in the building itself.

The power plant's interior affords a setting for further visual commentary regarding the pervasive negligence that characterizes company standards for disposing of nuclear waste. A recurring joke in interior scenes is the visual image of open barrels leaking bright green radioactive waste. The plant's inner recesses are overrun with barrels strewn about the halls and open areas of the plant. Painfully bright green waste, a caricature of radioactive refuse, leaks out of the barrels and even out of the trash can in the plant's coffee room (Gewirtz, 1991). The confluence of visual argument with the comic frame establishes the symbolic meaning of the leaking waste as an animated eyesore. The pervasive images of waste enhance the visual argument symbolized in the barrels. The images position the environmental rhetoric within a burlesque comic frame, which reveals the absurdity of the publicly ignored biohazard. That is, the conspicuous barrels reveal the neglect exhibited by their inadequate disposal of the barrels, and the obvious environmental hazard that they pose. The entire scene indicates the derelict administration of safety concerns.

The plant's employees remain oblivious to the adverse situation. Their blasé attitudes enhance the situation's comedic appeal. The more egregious methods of waste disposal demonstrate the comedic effect of the employees' general apathy. Lenny and Karl, Homer's coworkers, push wheelbarrows of nuclear waste down the hallways. As Lenny and Karl discuss proper locations and methods for disposal, one of the wheelbarrows crashes into a cement column and overturns. Lenny and Karl look at each other, shrug their shoulders, and continue down the hall. The waste from the overturned container spreads ominously through the passage, while the workers resume their labor, apparently unaware of the toxic spill. That the employees rarely notice the plant's production of waste adds humorous appeal to this visual image, and contributes to the show's rhetorical condemnation of unsound disposal practices. *The Simpsons* mocks the nuclear safety precautions typified in the overwhelming lack of concern for the hazards of radioactive waste. Leaking radioactive waste is a visual symbol intended to evoke criticism of the pervasive human disregard for the environment.

This social criticism is made more explicit within a burlesque comedic frame, in a parody of safety videos on nuclear energy. *The Simpsons* relies on the burlesque comic frame to render its explicit criticism of current standard practices of nuclear waste disposal. In Springfield's caricature of pro-nukes propaganda, Smilin' Joe Fission describes the preferred method of disposal for nuclear waste: "I'll just put it where nobody'll find it for a million years" (Kogen & Wolodarsky, 1990). This parody represents the typical "out of sight, out of mind" strategy for waste disposal, and attacks the general disregard for the environmental consequences of nuclear waste disposal. The show uses humor to reveal the ridiculousness of such careless disposal strategies—clarifying the obvious problems with improper disposal, and subsequent disregard for the possible environmental consequences. *The Simpsons* employs a comic frame to expose the failings of the social order, and to criticize the audiences' complicity in the normalization of such environmentally unsafe methods. By making light of the impact of nuclear accidents and contamination of the environment, the show forces the audience to adopt a critical eye regarding real social practices that mirror the environmental negligence of the citizens of Springfield. In this way, the show's writers comment on the general human view of the environment and the anthropocentric methods that govern the power plant's safety code.

Through the comic frame, *The Simpsons* carefully balances harsh criticism of American bureaucratic institutions and sardonic commentary of individual consumptive habits. "The comic frame inherently bypasses the extremes of the bureaucratic mindset...Further, the comic frame allows observation of oneself, recognizing one's own failures and limitations" (Madesen, 1993, p. 171). Members of the audience recognize themselves in the show's characters, gaining perspective on the limits and failures of their own actions. Through this self-observation, the comic frame engenders enlightened criticism of the symbolic relationships that ground social action. The comic frame enables *The Simpsons* to rhetorically connect the economic motivations for environmental exploitation with the normalizing power of profit-driven bureaucratic social institutions that foster individual anthropocentric practices. The nuclear plant  symbolizes tension between economic and environmental concerns. The plant represents the exploitation of environmental resources for wealth and power. Mr. Burns' priorities, exhibited in his operation of the plant, exemplify the attitude of economic elites and resource barons toward environmental concerns. Burns' methods of operation reveal the assumptions of characters represented by his prototype that environmental concerns are irreconcilable with economic interests. Furthermore, Burns uses his money and power to manipulate the image of his plant in order to make the environmental pollution more salient to the public.

At times *The Simpsons* abandons this charitable attitude in favor of a rhetoric well beyond the boundaries of Burke's comic frame, adopting a satiric or even burlesque style. *The Simpsons'* successful use of the burlesque comic frame is nowhere more evident than in the second season when Bart and Lisa catch a three-eyed fish while fishing near the Springfield Nuclear Reactor (Simon & Swartzwelder, 1990). When the event becomes public, a federal safety inspection team investigates the plant's emissions. In proper burlesque form, the episode chronicles the ludicrous findings of the inspection team: gum used to seal a crack in the coolant tower, a plutonium rod used as a paper-weight, monitoring stations unattended, and nuclear waste shin-deep in the hallways. The Feds threaten to shut down the power plant unless Burns makes significant improvements. Rather than bring his plant up to standard, Burns runs for governor, intending to use his elected power to keep the plant open. Inevitably confronted with Blinky, the three-eyed fish—a travesty of the ecological impacts of nuclear pollution, Burns hires spin doctors to boost his public image. In a brilliant burlesquc dialogue, Burns exacerbates Blinky's parodic symbolism with his dramatic interpretation of the fish's mutation as an evolutionary advance, based on the outlandish premise that three eyes are better than two.

> *Mr. Burns*: I'm here to talk to you about my little friend, here. Blinky. Many of you consider him to be a hideous genetic mutation. Well, nothing could be further from the truth. But don't take my word for it, let's ask an actor portraying Charles Darwin what he thinks.
>
> *Darwin*: Hello, Mr. Burns.
>
> *Burns*: Oh, hello Charles. Be a good fellow and tell our viewers about your theory of natural selection.
>
> *Darwin*: Glad to, Mr. Burns. You see, every so often Mother Nature changes her animals, giving them bigger teeth, sharper claws, longer legs, or in this case, a third eye. And if these variations turn out to be an improvement, the new animals thrive and multiply and spread across the face of the earth.
>
> *Burns*: So you're saying this fish might have an advantage over other fish, that it may in fact be a kind of super-fish.
>
> *Darwin*: I wouldn't mind having a third eye, would you? (Simon & Swartzwelder, 1990, in Groening, 1997, p. 38).

Mr. Burns' narrative continues the farcical tone of this episode, and performs a lampoon of evolutionary theory. Appealing to the authority of (an actor playing) Charles Darwin, Burns dismisses Blinky's (the so-called super-fish) state as a "hideous" blunder by Mother Nature. He characterizes Blinky's extra eye as an improvement on Mother Nature's original creation, and explains the mutation as the result of the evolutionary process of natural selection that begets superfish like Blinky. This imparts an explicit visual argument in the image of the fish, and articulates a profound contradiction to the verbal text uttered by Mr. Burns. The triply endowed animated fish visually "voices" opposition to Mr. Burns' claims, and through its own vivid image conveys the heinous maltreatment suffered by innumerable other animals in the same predicament in another location. The burlesque form of this episode exposes the outlandish excuses for the plant's pollution, and offers insightful ecological commentary on several levels. Human pollution is characterized as an improvement on nature, and human progress is viewed as an integral part of human evolution. These references articulate specific criticism of current environmental regulations, specifically the lax enforcement of the regulations concerning the dumping, safe storage, and disposal of nuclear waste. Furthermore, this episode condemns the manipulation of political and economic power to disguise ecological accountability and to shift blame for environmental problems. The show comments on the lack of adherence to safety standards for the plant, and criticizes the apathetic acceptance of unenforced environmental inspections. Finally, this episode explicitly criticizes media spin-doctors who distort the impacts of ecological degradation caused by wealthy corporations such as the nuclear power plant. *The Simpsons* artfully employs a burlesque comic frame to condemn the established social order that promotes media distortion of public knowledge, while encouraging self-criticism for viewers to recognize their own fallibility in the show's parody of the disingenuous politics of the resource elites.

As an icon of televised popular culture, *The Simpsons* offers critical social commentary on human experience. The show remarks on the cultural, social, and political ramifications of human activity, in recognizing the limitations of exploitative human existence. "*The Simpsons* works to encourage, critique, demanding that viewers be active in their consumption" (Korte, 1997, p. 3). *The Simpsons* characterizes human activity in an incriminating light, questioning established social institutions and normalized behaviors of the dominant societal frames. The show fosters social change by providing the audience the opportunity to recognize the shortcomings of their own living practices and alter their behavior accordingly. This self-critical observation fosters a charitable attitude toward the motivations of others. The comic frame thus promotes cooperative discussion, rather than tragic blame assignment that offers no possibility for social transcendence. Certainly comic framing exposes the bureaucratic power in everyday life and creates an ironic awareness of hierarchical absurdities, but the comic frame remains charitable rather than tragic, always assuming that negotiation of environmental issues is possible. Some environmental issues, however, inevitably have tragic consequences and may be impossible to reconcile. The comic frame endows us with a sense of social awareness, but it does not necessarily promote social activism. Toward this end, *The Simpsons* offers a critical view of the dominant attitude toward nature and exposes the dangers of human-centered practices. The show's rhetorical message fosters social transformation through comedy—revealing the negative social value of anti-environmentalism in a humorous light, which conveys the potential for positive social change. The comic frame offers a dynamic vision of humanity, and thus precludes the defeatism promoted by a static view of human activity that forecloses the possibility of cooperative action. As a televised communication medium, *The Simpsons* encourages the audience to engage in such dramatistic analysis to infer the implications of the show's humorous message.

SPRINGFIELD'S OTHER CREATURES: THE ROLE AND FATE OF ANIMALS IN *THE SIMPSONS*

Through the comic frame, *The Simpsons* exposes the ecological implications of numerous types of human-animal relationships, and comments on socially accepted practices of animal exploitation. The series offers countless opportunities for rhetorical criticism, but to maintain the close focus of this project, this section analyzes two episodes which provide the richest comedic visual text for an informed rhetorical analysis: the show's portrayal of eating and wearing animals.

In perhaps its most vivid expression of ecological commentary, *The Simpsons* chronicles Lisa's social transformation to a vegetarian lifestyle after she correlates the cute baby lamb she met at the petting zoo with the lamb chop on her dinner plate (Cohen, 1995). When her new lifestyle becomes public, Lisa is constantly under attack, most notably at school, where she is shown an outdated film encouraging the consumption of meat. A production of the beef industry, the film presents a comical depiction of the production of meat that scorns children who do not abide by the dominant social norms that compel consumption of animals. While the film offers a humorous view of dietary norms, it has a dark humor appeal because the film parody exhibits strident similarities with the meat industry's propaganda in the real world. Lisa is further ridiculed at Homer's barbecue where she is scorned for serving gazpacho, a vegetarian soup. The barbecue scene should resonate with vegetarian viewers as a depiction of the ubiquitous resistance to the provision of a vegetarian-friendly menu that offers meatless options in widely diverse social situations. At the barbecue, Lisa endures ridicule from her family as well as the guests, and she retaliates by attempting to vandalize the pig roasting on the rotisserie grill. Lisa's efforts to plunder the barbecue are themselves botched, propelling the entire barbecue—pig, pit, and all—on an airborne trajectory, ruining the year's most momentous social event, in Homer's estimation. The slapstick humor of the barbecue scene employs Burke's comedic frame, and facilitates the self-observation of the audience, questioning socially constructed dietary norms. Through humor, the cookout scene reveals the calamity of intolerance of diverse lifestyles; both Lisa and Homer—representing opposite extremes of the dietary conflict—exhibited a remarkable lack of tolerance for the eating preferences of their counterparts. This egotistic clash destroyed the carnivorous and vegetarian options, demonstrating the need for socially accommodating conditions to facilitate mutual satisfaction.

As the episode continues, Lisa endures an inner conflict about whether she should pursue her individual preferences or admit defeat in a culture inundated with propaganda pushing consumption of meat. Succumbing to this social pressure to eat flesh, Lisa eats a hot dog at the Kwik-E-Mart, but is informed it is a tofu hot dog, so she has not yet compromised her personal environmental code. She then meets Paul and Linda McCartney, who school Lisa in the etiquette of good vegetarianism, respecting others' choices, yet remaining vigilant in one's protest of animal consumption. Lisa's earlier inner conflict is resolved as she reconciles her personal convictions with tolerance for the personal decisions of others. Through Lisa's struggle to resist dominant social norms, this episode sheds light on the inherent incongruity between individual experience and socially constructed normative practices. This is an essential use of the comic frame: to divest one's own fallibility and attain an enriched perspective of the established order and its incumbent social and cultural values.

The concurrence of visual argument and the application of the comic frame in *The Simpsons* establish the potency of this program's environmental message. The episodic commentary on Lisa's vegetarianism exemplifies the rich text of the show as a productive multi-dimensional environmental commentary. At a base level, the show critiques social and cultural norms that vigorously condone the rampant consumption of animals. Through the narration of Lisa's struggle for a dietary choice, this episode reveals the marginalized perspective of vegetarians, which is relegated to the periphery of public discourse by the hegemonic culture of consumption. At another level, this narrative employs the comedic frame to humorously interpret the discrimination suffered by vegetarians and other dissidents against animal cruelty, for instance. The show offers a comedic interpretation of the marginalization of individuals who publicly hold counter-cultural ideals and are ridiculed and ostracized for their lifestyles. This episode reveals the personal suffering of marginalized individuals to promote a culture of social tolerance, and also articulates a formative experience that facilitates the social identification of dissident individuals through common experience who persevere in the knowledge that they are not alone. Through this comedic frame, *The Simpsons* presents a critical view of human exploitation of animals, enabling the audience to perceive the excessiveness of common practices. The program enjoys such significant persuasive influence because fundamentally the show is self-critical, exerting subtle rhetorical messages to promote positive social change.

Another preeminent episode critically comments on the subordinate position of nonhuman animals perpetuated by the extermination of animals expressly for the sartorial value of their coats. Mr. Burns represents the socially established and extremely affluent upper class. He demonstrates an unbridled consumptive appetite, and his social practices are marked by exploitative tactics of manipulation that establish his disregard for persons of inferior social status (all of Springfield). Mr. Burns enjoys the privileged position of a resource elite and exhibits his privilege through excessively wasteful habits that neglect ecological conservation. Aside from his customary exploitative disposition, Mr. Burns displays a unique perspective for rhetorical analysis in his flagrant desire to destroy animals for their fur (Scully, 1995). To realize his special penchant for a fur tuxedo, Burns steals the Simpsons' litter of twenty-five puppies. This episode's literary allusion to *101 Dalmatians* is testament to *The Simpsons'* profound pop-cultural allegory, and points to the significance of the synthesis of visual argument and the comic frame in this pop-cultural, televisual text.

The episode's predominant feature is a musical number performed by Mr. Burns extolling the virtue of wearing fur. Lisa and Bart observe Burns' performance from a window where they learn of his plans for their puppies. As external witnesses to Burns' theatrics, Lisa and Bart are a cruelty-conscious counterpoint to Burns' exploitative extravagance. The children possess a contrapuntal function to Burns' gleeful display—that is, they represent a socially conscious stance in disapproval of Burns' plans to exorcise the puppies. Bart and Lisa, who remain mostly silent spectators precluded from occupying space inside Mr. Burns' room, offer a critical perspective to the television audience through visual argument. Viewers identify with the spatial positioning of Bart and Lisa's visual images because Bart and Lisa's positioning as critical observers parallels the audience's relation to the animated reality of Springfield as critical observers.

Bart and Lisa, as critical observers of Burns' flaunted excessive consumerism, serve as intermediaries to the contested practice of fur consumption. Through their mediating role and the spatial position of their visual images, the Simpson children perform an argumentative function. Bart and Lisa are positioned in physical opposition to Mr. Burns' stage (his closet), in a visual representation of social criticism against fur. The symbolic force of the children's visual images comes from the rhetorical power of their counterpoint to Burns. In addition, their discursive space on the second stage of the television itself, their spatial position, empowers the television audience to adopt similar roles as critical observers. The rhetorical tactics of the visual argument of this scene should ideally foster critical commentary regarding the ecological implications of killing animals for their pelts, and thus induce environmentally conscious change.

Mr. Burns provides a verbal text to add meaning to the pictorial, spatial arguments of the scene. He offers the perspective of guiltless consumption that is associated with the implications of environmental degradation. Unconcerned with socially responsible behavior, Mr. Burns sings a song that offers a riotous commentary on the fur trade. "See My Vest" is a hysterical musical number in which Mr. Burns models his wardrobe, making the argument for human wearing of animals. The song is a litany of animal skins and appendages including the title item, a vest "made from real gorilla chest." Mr. Burns describes the softness of his sweater made from "authentic Irish Setter," the elegance of his vampire bat evening-wear, and the warmth of his "grizzly bear underwear." He sings of his "albino African endangered rhino" slippers, his poodle beret, his loafers made of gophers, the hat that was his cat, and his plethora of turtlenecks (literally). Mr. Burns ends the song celebrating the magnificence of his "greyhound fur tuxedo," adding two dogs should be saved for "matching clogs" (Scully, 1995, in Groening, 1997, p. 172).

Burns celebrates his successful acquisition of his impressive collection of clothing exclusively tailored from genuine animal pelts. He sings a lyrical commentary on the pleasure of owning such luxurious garments, and emphasizes the authenticity of these literally "wild" fabrics. The application of the comic frame is evident in the witty rhyming scheme coupled with the lyrical revelry of such outlandish social practices. The comic effect of Burns' eccentric performance is enhanced by the conflation of his morbid subject matter and his jubilant attitude. Burns plays the clown in this episode, performing a comic ritual that highlights social discrepancies, which warrant conscious action. The incongruity of the song's textual and musical elements articulates comedy's usefulness to identify the absurdity of normative social practice. Burns' whimsical inflection belies the literal meaning of his words, and exposes the absurdity of his message. In this way, Burns presents a farcical rendition of human consumption that fosters meaningful critical commentary through the composition of Burns' comedic message and the visual argument of Bart and Lisa's spatial position.

The Simpsons' environmental rhetoric demonstrates the power of the comic frame in pop-culture analysis, enabling the audience to see through "the obfuscation of the bureaucratic, while opening space for discourse by the minority and marginalized voices in society" (Madsen, 1993, p. 171). The comic frame exhibits a two-pronged approach for effective rhetorical commentary: exposing social ills while creating a new discursive space to incorporate marginalized opinions into the public sphere. Through comedic expression, *The Simpsons* presents a complicated environmental message. That message presents enlightened criticism of the hegemonic assumptions of the existing social order, while simultaneously maintaining a self-critical attitude that facilitates a re-conceptualization of social and cultural relationships that grounds social action.

NATURE AS IDEOLOGY: *THE SIMPSONS'* PRIME-TIME ECO-CRITIQUE

This detailed investigation into the meaning of *The Simpsons* seeks to identify the show's environmental message. Granted, most viewers might not impart such significance from thirty minutes of their prime-time experience. Determining the audience's understanding of the environmental message is admittedly difficult. Such critical analysis is crucial, however, to increasing public awareness of mediated discourse. Madsen describes the critic's ultimate task to alter social frames, which increases the chance for constructive social change (Madsen, 1993, p. 170). Such endeavors help foster more informed television audience members who recognize their situation as passive subjects to the manipulation of media messages to influence and direct their behavior as consumers. *The Simpsons'* antics "mirror even our culture's most unrecognized aspects in all its tiny facets. So even if the viewer does not manage to grasp all the messages transmitted by the series' characters, he or she is always very likely to at least decode some of them" (Steiger, 1999, p. 13). *The Simpsons'* success results from a combination of rhetorical elements, which projects more than mere entertainment into America's living rooms (Steiger, 1999, p. 3). In this way, the show educates its audience while maintaining popular appeal through its humorous, animated form. The series has transferred the expression of political opinion from traditional sources such as radio, and newspapers, to television (Steiger, 1999, p. 13).

The powerful symbolic influence of *The Simpsons* is enhanced through its unique synthesis of comedic and visual rhetorical elements. Televisual media enables a critical look at the complexities of human experience through the manipulation of verbal, acoustic and visual dramatic elements. The combination of these different sense experiences creates a powerfully realistic portrayal of familiar human situations. "By animating *The Simpsons*, Groening managed to reach a higher degree of realism, while he is still entertaining and thus appealing to his audience" (Steiger, 1999, p. 4). The complex symbolism of comic and visual media presents a multidimensional perspective of reality that enjoys powerful rhetorical appeal. Televised reality enjoys an attractiveness that enables persuasive arguments against dominant social and cultural norms. The realism of televisual media is particularly persuasive when offering critical commentary against institutions and practices familiar to America's television audience. *The Simpsons* presents an alternative epistemology that critiques the environmental practices sanctioned by dominant social norms. Through the complex manipulation of multidimensional rhetorical elements, the series reveals the ecological impacts of human activity. The subversive symbolism of *The Simpsons'* environmental rhetoric functions as enlightened criticism of cultural norms of consumption, which exonerate society's ecocidal practices.

The Simpsons presents a strong ideological message about nature as a symbol—as an object for human exploitation. The characters of *The Simpsons* display an overall disregard for the environment, are separated from nature, and often oppose nature. The show portrays the mainstream culture in which the environment has a solely utilitarian value and exists exclusively for human purposes. Through humorous exaggeration, *The Simpsons* offers critical commentary on humanity and points out the danger of destroying the environment. The series' message is revolutionary because it portrays the counterculture of environmental activism as an alternative to anthropocentrism. *The Simpsons'* activism is communicated effectively through the juxtaposition of characters that represent the extremes on an ecological spectrum. Homer represents anthropocentrism, the quintessential exploitative human. Homer's character has a powerful dramatic function: increasing viewers' awareness by evoking reactions to his naivete to media influence of popular culture (Steiger, 1999, p. 5).

Lisa counters Homer's egregious anthropocentrism and symbolizes an environmental ethic of caring for nonhuman creatures. Lisa represents a moral center to the show, which enables her to reveal the irony of her father's anthropocentric actions. When Lisa bemoans the crashing of an oil tanker on Baby Seal Beach, Homer comforts her and reveals his anthropocentric perspective: "It'll be okay, honey. There's lots more oil where that came from" (Appel, 1996). Homer, not considering the ecological implications of the oil spill, instead thinks of the effects on human access to resources.

Through humor, each character's commentary functions differently; Lisa presents a moral force that opposes Homer's flagrant anthropocentrism and effectively points out the absurdity of human action. In this way, the show offers the chance for positive social change. The comic frame permits observation of ourselves, while maintaining the possibility for action by increasing societal consciousness (Carlson, 1986, p. 447). *The Simpsons* is a subversive look at the state of human existence, but is effective because of its chosen methods of rhetorical commentary. The visual communication of the show makes its criticism palatable. The show's writers are well aware that the "pastel colors of animation often blind the censors to their biting critiques of the world" (Korte, 1997, p. 7). "Combining entertainment and subversion, *The Simpsons* angers some people as much as it amuses others...Joe Rhodes of *Entertainment Weekly* notes that '*The Simpsons* at its heart...is guerrilla TV, a wicked satire masquerading as a prime-time cartoon'" (Korte, 1997, p. 9). Through its unique rhetorical methods, *The Simpsons* describes the environmental harms of social ills. Through the humorous interpretations of Springfield's environmental hazards and the moral force of Lisa's portrayal of environmental activism, the show offers an alternative solution to exploitative human practices.

The Simpsons functions as a form of environmental activism and thus reveals popular culture's effectiveness as a medium for ecological commentary. The show increases public awareness of environmental issues, and educates the television audience while entertaining them. "Unlike many shows on TV, *The Simpsons* works to encourage critique, demanding that viewers be active in their consumption" (Korte, 1997, p. 3). Through humor, the show reveals the anthropocentrism of human activity in such a way that otherwise harsh criticism is palatable and potentially effects social change. By pointing out the humorous fallacies in human action, the series offers a significant look at the life of the typical American family, and in this way profoundly impacts the attitudes and beliefs of the television audience. The crude animation of *The Simpsons* transcends conventional boundaries of environmental rhetoric. The series embodies a powerful social force by presenting a multidimensional message that critically comments on institutions and practices of the normative social and cultural context, and engages the audience through rhetorical appeals to viewers' personal experiences.

REFERENCES

Andrews, J.R. (1990). *The Practice of Rhetorical Criticism.* White Plains, NY: Longman.

Appel, R. (1996, November 24). Bart after dark (D. Polcino, Director). In J.L. Brooks, M. Groening, & S. Simon (Executive Producers), *The Simpsons.* New York: Twentieth Century Fox Film Corporation.

Blair, J.A. (1996). The possibility and actuality of visual arguments. *Argumentation and Advocacy.* 33, 23-29.

Burke, K. (1950). *A Rhetoric of Motives.* Berkeley: University of California Press.

Burke, K. (1959). *Attitudes Toward History.* Boston: Beacon Press.

Burke, K. (1966). *Language as Symbolic Action: Essays on Life, Literature, and Method.* Berkeley: University of California Press.

Carlson, A.C. (1986). Gandhi and the comic frame: "Ad bellum purificandum". *Quarterly Journal of Speech*, 72, 446-445.

Cohen, D.S. (1995, October 15). Lisa the vegetarian (M. Kirkland, Director). In J.L. Brooks, M. Groening, & S. Simon (Executive Producers), *The Simpsons.* New York: Twentieth Century Fox Film Corporation.

Gewirtz, J. (1991, October 17). Homer defined (M. Kirkland, Director). In J.L. Brooks, M. Groening, S. Simon (Executive Producers), *The Simpsons.* New York: Twentieth Century Fox Film Corporation.

Groening, M. (1997). *The Simpsons: A Complete Guide to our Favorite Family.* R. Richmond & A. Coffman (Eds.), Harper Perennial: New York.

Groening, M. (1999). *The Simpsons Forever: A Complete Guide to our Favorite Family...Continued.* S.M. Gimple (Ed.), Harper Perennial: New York.

Gronbeck, B.E. (1995). Unstated propositions: Relationships among verbal, visual and acoustic languages. In S. Jackson (Ed.), *Argumentation and Values* (pp. 539-542). Annandale, VA: Speech Communication Association.

Klumpp, J.F. & Hollihan, T. (1989). Rhetorical criticism as moral action. *Quarterly Journal of Speech*, 75, 84-97.

Kogen, J. & Wolodarsky, W. (1990, January 21). Homer's odyssey (W. Archer, Director). In J.L. Brooks, M. Groening, & S. Simon (Executive Producers), *The Simpsons.* New York: Twentieth Century Fox Film Corporation.

Korte, D. (1997). *The Simpsons* as quality television. *The Simpsons Archive* [On-line]. Available: http://www.snpp.com/other/papers/dk.paper.html

Madsen, A. (1993). The comic frame as a corrective to bureaucratization: A dramatistic perspective on argumentation. *Argumentation and Advocacy*, 29, 64-177.

Scully, M. (1995, April 9). Two dozen and one greyhounds (B. Anderson, Director). In J.L. Brooks, M. Groening, & S. Simon (Executive Producers), *The Simpsons.* New York: Twentieth Century Fox Film Corporation.

Simon, S. & Swartzwelder, J. (1990, November 1). Two Cars in every Garage and Three Eyes on every Fish (W. Archer, Director). In J.L. Brooks, M. Groening, & S. Simon (Executive Producers), *The Simpsons.* New York: Twentieth Century Fox Film Corporation.

Steiger, G. (1999). *The Simpsons* - just funny or more? *The Simpsons Archive* [On-line]. Available: http://www.snpp.com/other/papers/gs.paper.html

In her essay, Todd argues in part that *The Simpsons* uses humor to offer up a cutting cultural critique of the way we treat the environment. Do some brainstorming or some online searching to find another humorous text (this could be a clip from a TV show, a film, or a stand-up act, among other possibilities) that makes a claim about an environmental issue. Bring this text to class and present it to your classmates, explaining the argument you see emerging there.

What is Todd's analytical argument about *The Simpsons*? What support does she marshal to make this case? What details does she use from the episodes themselves?

Todd makes much of the character Lisa Simpson's ability to create social commentary on human treatment of animals and the environment. Watch an episode or two of *The Simpsons* (you might consider watching "Lisa the Vegetarian" from season 7, which Todd describes in her essay) and write a short essay in which you describe Lisa's environmental ethos. What characteristics does she possess? Do these characteristics endear her and her beliefs to you? Why or why not?

On its website, ecoAmerica describes itself as a non-profit organization whose goal it is to build "awareness, understanding and action for environmental solutions among mainstream Americans." The organization produced Climate and Energy Truths *in April 2009 to help "climate solutions advocates ... enhance and unify their communications." What follows are excerpts from that report.*

excerpts from *CLIMATE AND ENERGY TRUTHS: OUR COMMON FUTURE*

BY ECOAMERICA

MAKING THE CONNECTIONS

With major climate legislation pending in the U.S. Congress and the upcoming round of the United Nations IPCC Copenhagen round of negotiations, 2009 will be a seminal year in solving climate change. Success in these forums will depend on the strength of public support for new energy and climate solutions. Progressive advocates need to adopt the strongest possible themes and messaging on the common truths issues.

The coal and oil lobby has been very successful in communicating a seemingly moderate and comprehensive approach to our energy problems, suggesting that they support alternative energy and "all of the above." Their values-based messaging has resulted in a significant shift in public sentiment moving toward embracing more domestic drilling for oil, both on and offshore, and more coal and nuclear energy. Opinion research has also consistently shown that while growing numbers of Americans believe climate change is real and a threat, the saliency of this issue is low and the debate is often polarizing.

Too often, climate solutions advocates work the base (elites) while ignoring mainstream Americans. And when we do talk to swing voters or encourage our base to reach out, typically we lack effective, emotionally compelling language on these issues. Meanwhile, proponents of carbon-based fuels have started to attack climate change solution policies, like cap and trade, as a tax that will fall on consumers. Without effective countervailing communications, these critiques could sink any hope of passing legislation that combats climate change.

ecoAmerica conducted the "Climate and Energy Truths: Our Common Future" research project to address this challenge. Our goal was to develop market-tested language that we could provide to climate solutions advocates and elected officials so that they have the tools to move public opinion and support. We also wanted to provide a shared lexicon to substitute for the cacophony that interferes with effective "branding."

The messages we developed are designed to capture attention, raise concerns, offer solutions, and inspire hope and enthusiasm for immediate solutions to our climate and energy problems. We sought to identify effective and ineffective phrases to capture climate change and our new energy future in ways that resonate with Americans at a core-value level and neutralize the opposition's framing of the issues.

"Climate and Energy Truths" advocates and provides a more disciplined approach to communications. Many of the concepts here may seem familiar, but in practice, most of us rely on traditional policy arguments that resonate well with traditional environmentalists but are neutral to counter-productive with swing voters.

EXECUTIVE SUMMARY

America needs to move rapidly toward the clean, unlimited, efficient, job-producing, prosperity-inducing energies of the 21st century that will eliminate our reliance on dirty fuels and our dependence on the hostile, foreign regimes that profit from them. It's time for a renewed period of American prosperity at home and economic and political leadership around the world.

Oil and coal interests now claim ownership of energy independence, comprehensive solutions, and responsible treatment of the earth—things to which they are, in reality, opposed. Environmentalists might not have great economic credibility, but Americans believe them when they 'point and shame' bad environmental practices. Oil and coal companies should be challenged to explain how their policies foster what they claim in the face of steadily increasing dependence on foreign oil and their almost exclusive reliance on fossil fuels.

The side that stands on the mountaintop of values in this debate will defeat the side that has to defend its specific positions, policies or fuel sources. We need to claim the high ground, play offense, and let the other side play defense.

Our research reveals clear strategiess for communicating the need for environmentally sound ways of addressing our climate and energy challenges. Attitudes on these topics are highly malleable with good messaging. Knowing themes, like "American leadership" is not enough. Unity and discipline through consistent and effective wording and sequence is absolutely necessary to move public opinion. Starting with values, and paying attention to specific words and sequencing, can make messages much more effective.

Communicating to the environmental base in 'green code' makes us incapable of talking with anyone but ourselves. The language and concepts in this report are designed to move mainstream or swing American voters as well as the environmental 'base,' and it should be employed with both.

- Voters are more energized around the energy debate than the climate change debate, but they can become engaged in climate to the extent that they see it as part of energy or pollution, or related to other values and concerns.
- Messaging on both energy and climate change is much stronger when it uses values-oriented language rather than a technical or policy-oriented approach or when we debate science. More so than in many areas we have seen, activating multiple values tends to be stronger then just invoking a single value.
- For climate change, leading with global warming, climate crisis or climate change tends to polarize and weaken the message. The language itself is especially problematic among swing voters. We should speak of deteriorating atmosphere and only after establishing connections with Americans' other values first.
- Climate messages are successful when they connect to other themes such as energy independence, reducing dependence on foreign oil, and safe and natural forms of energy that never run out. Linking climate change to pollution and our families' health is a strong approach to garnering support for climate solutions.
- Aspirational messages that tap into American exceptionalism, American ingenuity, American energy independence, American jobs, "freedom"

and America's future are powerful messages on both energy and climate change. Voters like any language calling on America to "lead."

- Stay away from debating weather since voters have alternative explanations or debate the causes of hurricanes, droughts, and floods.
- Stay away from debating science or specific policies. Voters believe that there are many sides to the science and question it. There is no debate around the desirability of dealing with pollution, protecting our families' health, and developing new clean and safe energy.
- As on many polarizing issues, on climate messages, it is important to recognize and address people's ambivalence while communicating a positive message about how we can address problems. Strong language includes: *We can argue about the causes of what we're seeing, but scientists agree there's something we can do about it.*
- The best new term is "deteriorating atmosphere" or "our deteriorating atmosphere" (personalizing the term) instead of 'global warming' or 'climate crisis'.
- We can successfully and should repeatedly characterize coal as "dirty" and nuclear as "unsafe." Our best approach; however, is to embed these issues in a broader, comprehensive approach to energy that is environmentally sound and economically advantageous. We win far more strongly by fighting on the terrain of clean, safe energy than by debating specific technologies considered one at a time.
- It does not work particularly well to talk about the specific amount of money we will save, the cost of fuel, specific mileage standards, etc. Again, getting "into the weeds" of policy increases voters' concerns and levels the playing field to the advantage of the opposition.
- Cap and Trade is unfamiliar to voters and support is relatively weak when voters are presented with a brief description. Referring to a cap and trade proposal as a *Clean Energy Dividend, Clean Energy Cash-Back, Pollution Penalty, or Pollution Reduction Refund* is strongly preferable to using the term, Cap and Trade.
- We should not differentiate multiple forms of pollution. We want the public to see that the issue is whether we're going to move toward clean, safe, natural, unlimited sources of energy that protect the Earth and our health or dangerous, dirty energy that endangers both our national and economic security.

The findings of the ecoAmerica study posit that the phrases "global warming," "climate crisis," and "climate change" make for a weak environmental message when it comes to appealing to swing voters. The best new term, they say, is "deteriorating atmosphere." Why do you think this is a more successful term for communicating a message about threats to the environment? Can you think of any other phrases that might be successful? Why do you think so?

Based on the findings of the ecoAmerica study, write a short essay in which you comment on the power of language for creating concrete social, political, and environmental change.

After reading the excerpts from ecoAmerica's report carefully, discuss with a small group the organization's findings and suggestions. Then, working together, examine the language choices made by news media, politicians, and advocacy groups as they discuss environmental issues. What differences do you see in the ways that these sources talk about the environment?

In September 2009, Seed *magazine editor Maywa Montenegro interviewed maverick environmentalist and self-described "tech-loving Green" Stewart Brand just ahead of the publication of Brand's latest book,* Whole Earth Discipline: An Ecopragmatist Manifesto. *(You can find an annotated version of the book online at http://web.me.com/stewartbrand/DISCIPLINE_footnotes/Contents.html.) Brand's piece "Reframing the Problems," from* The Clock of the Long Now: Time and Responsibility, *begins on page 167.*

A MANIFESTO FOR THE PLANET

BY MAYWA MONTENEGRO

Stewart Brand is a rare breed of environmentalist: in his own words, "an ecologist by training, a futurist by profession, and a hacker (lazy engineer) at heart." In the 60s, Brand campaigned against nuclear power and staged a "Hunger Show" to dramatize the global famine predicted by his mentor, Paul Ehrlich, but he also began printing a decidedly pro-technology handbook for saving the planet. *Whole Earth Catalog*, first published in 1968, was premised on the notion that given the right information, tools, and awareness, people could—and would—create a more sustainable world. It was, many have said, the beginning of environmentalism.

Since that time, Brand's own views on core "green issues," from atomic energy to genetic engineering, have shifted under the weight of scientific evidence. Rather than quietly backpedal, Brand has now issued a bold challenge to the very movement he helped create: Can you forsake ideology for the good of the planet? *Whole Earth Discipline* contains every reason why they should: 300 pages of data, anecdotes, and arguments that illustrate, in withering detail, the scale of ecological problems we face today, and the utter inability of faith-based environmentalism alone to fix them. *Seed* editor Maywa Montenegro recently caught up with the 70-year-old Brand, ahead of a multi-city book tour.

Seed: It's been 40 years since the first edition of *Whole Earth Catalog.* Why publish the sequel now?

Stewart Brand: There was actually no periodicity. In fact, I kind of hate the "40 years later" stuff that's going on. But what did happen is the realization that I'd accumulated a set of contrarian views on some important environmental issues—specifically, cities, nuclear energy, genetic engineering, and geoengineering—and that it added up to a story worth telling.

That led me to the larger strategy of trying to move the environmental movement from a romantic identification with nature toward a more scientific basis. And moving on from that, toward an engineering approach to solving environmental problems.

Seed: Do you think environmentalists will be receptive?

SB: There are two main elements that are changing things. One is the younger generation, which is pretty comfortable with technology and doesn't regard it as inherently evil. So something like synthetic biology or genetic engineering looks like something they can figure out and put to use. And when it comes to nuclear engineering, they don't remember the Cold War or Chernobyl. The other element is climate change. It was taken seriously early and often by environmentalists, and they're now living with the consequences of having been right about it. They paid attention to climatologists, to the scientists, to the IPCC, so they are more comfortable with a scientific approach on other issues.

Seed: You've said that environmentalists have some "radical news" coming with urbanization, specifically in the developing world.

SB: Well, the good news is that people in cities in the developing world are having fewer children than they did when they were out in the bush. As they move from the bush, the bush is coming back. And they don't have, by and large, the kind of concerns that we have in the global north about genetic engineering and nuclear power.

Their dire need for grid electricity is pushing them right now to build vast quantities of coal-fired plants. But they are increasingly aware that this is a problem: Many developing countries are energetically pursuing nuclear power, which is the only immediate, one-for-one substitute.

Seed: Isn't nuclear power prohibitively expensive for most developing countries?

SB: My guess is that the developing world is going to be a major market for microreactors, for the new generation of small nuclear reactors. These offer grid electricity generated close to hand and pretty inexpensively. The smaller ones, the 35–150 megawatt ones, are the right size for a town of a certain scale. You can start with one, and as the town grows, or as people go up the energy ladder, you just add another and connect them all in sequence. Over time you get the benefits of a large reactor without having to build the whole thing from scratch. That kind of thing will be very attractive in developing economies.

On most environmental issues, a lot is going to be played out in the developing world because that's where the major needs and crises are. Also, that's where there is the ability to radically rethink things. We've seen this with cell phones. Wait 'til those folks get a hold of synthetic biology.

Seed: In the run-up to the Copenhagen summit in December, there's been increased debate over whether climate change is a regulation problem or an innovation problem. How do you see it?

SB: It's not an either/or question. We need science to understand the climate dynamics much better. We've got better data and better models than we used to, but when the predictions of the models fail, they fail in important and scary ways. They did not predict the melting of the Arctic ice; they're not particularly helpful in the melting of the sub-Arctic tundra. There may be an important negative feedback dynamic going on above the continents, where ever more woody plant growth is apparently fixing extra carbon. Just as important is understanding the oceans, particularly the microbes in the ocean and what they're doing. At what temperature does the ocean stratify and go relatively dead? We're short on good-enough data.

Then on the engineering level, direct intervention—geoengineering—is going to be necessary sooner than most people think or expect. Research there is absolutely essential because to make a mistake on the planetary scale is not something you want to do. Money and effort going into the 10 or 12 geoengineering schemes we have so far, plus developing new ones, is of the essence.

At the same time, government involvement is crucial because governments decide infrastructure—what the price of various energy forms is going to be. The American, European, Chinese, and Indian governments need to make coal expensive. If they don't, coal will be burned until we all cook.

Seed: Can you tell me about your vision of the Greens and the Turquoises?

SB: I question whether "green" or "environmentalist" will be a big enough tent to contain a growing variety of disunity within the modern environmental community. People who are fiercely against nuclear have very little good to say to someone who is otherwise totally green but likes nuclear.

So one approach is to say, okay, there are different flavors of green—the traditional "Greens" and this other thing. I wanted a name for them, so I just called them "Turquoises," mixing green and blue. There's enough work to keep both of them busy with more projects than they can possibly handle. Traditional Greens are already good at things like preserving, protecting, and restoring natural systems. The Turquoise types may be the ones who find new ways to push these projects in cities. Here I think they can collaborate completely, or almost completely.

When it comes to engineering technology, however, I'm not so sure. There's a fundamental difference between Greens who automatically distrust technology and Turquoises who automatically look at a technology as a potential tool. Something like synthetic biology comes along, and the Greens say, "Just a damn minute," while the Turquoises say, "Oh boy, this is interesting. I know what to do with this stuff." Greens are typically worriers, while the younger Turquoises are more interested in opportunity, so they grab things and say, "Let's try it out and we'll worry later." It's the *worry first* versus *worry later* dichotomy.

Seed: Where do you fit along this spectrum?

SB: I've been a tech-loving Green from day one. *Whole Earth Catalog* was a technology-accepting green publication. We were pushing what was called "appropriate technology"—solar, wind, and other things that at the time were viewed askance. Everybody in the environmental movement, for example, hated cars. Then Amory Lovins came along and said, actually we can make cars more efficient, which would change the energy picture in a huge way. Amory describes himself as a techno-twit. I'm just a somewhat older and more experienced techno-twit.

Seed: As a techno-twit, you've got some interesting plans for this book.

SB: Yes—I'm doing an online annotated version. It will go live at the same time that the book publishes in October. Basically, the sections of every chapter that are footnoted will be immersed in the research material with lots of live links and photos, diagrams, charts, and so on. So anyone who wants to see my sources can go straight there and draw their own conclusions.

And I'll try to keep updating the book. I've already got some additional levels of understanding from people like George Church and Larry Brilliant. I'll just add that to the online version.

Seed: You point out that Gaia will persist whether or not humans do. But are you optimistic about the future of people?

SB: I agree with Lovelock, who in 1938 said something terrible is coming and we're still figuring out what it is and what we're going to do about it. So, no, I'm not sanguine. If most of the things that I point at in the book are pursued full on, we'd have a pretty good chance, but I'm not sure that it's going to play out. It's not bad people. There's just a lot of momentum that we've built up going in directions that are now understood to be harmful and are getting more so as time goes by. You can't turn a big ship on a dime.

In the fall of 1968, Stewart Brand founded, edited, and published the Whole Earth Catalog, *a pioneering resource that changed the way many people thought about the environment (parts of the catalog are available online at http://www.wholeearth.com/index.php). "Reframing the Problems" is an excerpt from Brand's 2000 book* The Clock of the Long Now: Time and Responsibility, *which "challenges readers to get outside themselves and combat the short-term irresponsible thinking that has led to environmental destruction and social chaos," according to a* Publisher's Weekly *review. An interview with Brand begins on page 161.*

REFRAMING THE PROBLEMS

BY STEWART BRAND

In 1996, a suddenly growing multibillion-dollar California foundation asked me and others to write a short paper on the question, "What are the most serious environmental problems confronting humankind at the beginning of the twenty-first century?" Figuring I would have nothing original to add to that list, I decided to write the piece from the perspective of the Clock of the Long Now. *Looking from outside the present time gave a sideways rather than end-on view of the current environmental problems and invited rethinking them in terms of eventual practical solutions rather than only how great a threat they pose. I think the paper fits in at this point in the discussion, where the uses and advantages of long-view thinking are explored. The foundation (now the third-largest in America) is endowed with the wealth of David Packard, cofounder of Hewlett-Packard, the brilliantly successful electronics firm based in Palo Alto, California.*

To the David and Lucile Packard Foundation:

My contribution may be to bend your question a little. Environmental problems these days come in a pretty familiar litany of pretty familiar names. The World Population problem. Climate Change problem. Loss of Biodiversity. Ocean Fisheries. Freshwater Aquifers. North/South Economic Disparity. Rain Forests. Agricultural and Industrial Pollution. Identifying these issues and making them everyone's concern has been a major triumph of environmental science and activism in the late twentieth century.

I propose that the Packard Foundation could make a contribution beyond even the splendid effect of its funding by helping to rethink—reframe—the very structure of how environmental problems are stated. This is a common practice among inventive engineers such as the late Mr. Packard. When a design problem resists solution, reframe the problem in such a way that it invites solution.

An example of spontaneous reframing occurred in 1969, when the Apollo program began returning color photographs of the Earth from space. Everyone saw the photographs and saw that we occupied a planet that was beautiful, all one, very finite, and possibly fragile. The environmental movement took off from that moment—the first Earth Day was in 1970. That effect of the American space program was never intended or anticipated. Indeed, nearly all environmentalists in the sixties (except Jacques Cousteau) actively fought against the space program, saying that we had to solve Earth's problems before exploring space.

What might be some further helpful reframings?

(1) *Civilization's shortening attention span is mismatched with the pace of environmental problems.*

What with accelerating technology and the short-horizon perspective that goes with burgeoning market economics (next quarter) and the spread of democracy (next election), we have a situation where steady but gradual environmental degradation escapes our notice. The slow, inexorable pace of ecological and climatic cycles and lag times bear no relation to the hasty cycles and lag times of human attention, decision, and action. We can't slow down all of human behavior, and shouldn't, but we might slow down parts.

Now is the period in which people feel they live and act and have responsibility. For most of us *now* is about a week, sometimes a year. For some traditional tribes in the American northeast and Australia *now* is seven generations back and forward (175 years each direction). Just as the Earth photographs gave us a sense of *the big here*, we need things that give people a sense of *the long now*.

Candidate now-lengtheners might include: abiding charismatic artifacts; extreme longitudinal scientific studies; very large, slow, ambitious projects; human life extension (with delayable childbearing); some highly durable institutions; reward systems for slow responsible behavior; honoring patience and sometimes disdaining rush; widespread personal feeling for the span of history; planning practices that preserve options for the future.

In a sense, the task here is to make the world safe for hurry by slowing some parts way down.

> (2) *Natural systems can be thought of pragmatically as "natural infrastructure."*

One area in which governments and other institutions seem comfortable thinking in the long term is the realm of infrastructure, even though there is no formal economics of infrastructure benefits and costs. (There should be and could be.) We feel good about investing huge amounts in transportation systems, utility grids, and buildings.

Infrastructure thinking is directly transferable to natural systems. Lucky for us, we don't have to build the atmosphere that sustains us, the soils, the aquifers, the wild fisheries, the forests, the rich biological complexity that keeps the whole thing resilient. All we have to do is defend these systems—from ourselves. It doesn't take much money. It doesn't even take much knowledge, though knowledge certainly helps.

A bracing way to think about this matter would be to seriously take on the project of terraforming Mars—making it comfortable for life. Then think about reterraforming Earth if we lose the natural systems that previously built themselves here. The fact is that humans are now so powerful that we are in effect terraforming Earth. Rather poorly so far. We can't undo our power; it will only increase. We can terraform more intelligently—with a light, slow hand, and with the joy and pride that goes with huge infrastructure projects. Current efforts by the Army Corps of Engineers to restore the Florida Everglades, for example, have this quality.

(3) *Technology can be good for the environment.*

My old biology teacher, Paul Ehrlich, has a formula declaring that environmental degradation is proportional to "population times affluence times technology." It now appears that the coming of information technology is reversing that formula, so that better technology and more affluence leads to less environmental harm—*if* that is one of the goals of the society.

"Doing more with less"—Buckminister Fuller's "ephemeralization"—is creating vastly more efficient industrial and agricultural processes, with proportionately less impact on natural systems. It is also moving ever more of human activity into an *infosphere* less harmfully entwined with the biosphere.

Given its roots, the Packard Foundation is particularly well suited to evaluate and foster what a Buddhist engineer might call *right technology*. It would be helpful to assemble a roster of existing environmentally benign technologies. Satellites for communication and remote sensing come to mind. So does Jim Levelock's gas chromatograph (which detected atmospheric chlorofluorocarbons)—invented for Hewlett-Packard, as I recall.

The foundation might support activities such as Eric Drexler's Foresight Institute, which is aiming to shape nanotechnology (molecular engineering) toward cultural and environmental responsibility. It might support services on the Internet that distribute information and discussion about the environmental impacts of new and anticipated technologies and their interactions. Good effects should be investigated as well as ill effects.

(4) *Feedback is the primary tool for tuning systems, especially at the natural/artificial interface.*

German military officers are required to eat what their troops eat and after they eat. That single tradition assures that everyone's meals are excellent and timely, and it enhances unit morals, and respect for the officers. The feedback cycle is local and immediate, not routed through bureaucratic specialists or levels of hierarchy.

In similar fashion, factories, farms, and cities that pollute rivers and water tables could be required to release their outflows upstream of their own water intake rather than downstream.

The much-lamented "tragedy of the commons" is a classic case of pathological feedback—where each individual player is rewarded rather than punished for wasting the common resource. In fact, healthy self-governing commons systems are frequent in the world and in history, as examined in Elinor Ostrum's *Governing the Commons.* The commons she dissects include communally held mountain meadows and forests in Switzerland, irrigation cooperatives in Japan and Spain, and jointly managed fisheries in Turkey, Sri Lanka, and Nova Scotia. The successful ones are maintained (and maintainable) neither by the state nor the market but by a local set of community feedbacks adroitly tuned to ensure the system's long-term health and prosperity. Ostrum detects eight design principles that keep a wide variety of common systems self-balancing. They are: clear boundaries; locally appropriate rules; collective agreement; monitoring; graduated sanctions; conflict-resolution mechanisms; rights to organize; nested enterprises.

The Packard Foundation could encourage feedback analysis of environmental problems and help devise local-feedback solutions.

(5) *Environmental health requires peace, prosperity, and continuity.*

War, especially civil war, destroys the environment and displaces caring for the environment for generations. Widespread poverty destroys the environment and undermines all ability to think and act for the long term.

Environmental activists and peace activists are still catching on that they are natural partners, and both remain averse to business boosters who might aid prosperity. Peacekeeping soldiers are not in the mix at all. But for a culture and its environment to come into abiding equanimity you need all four—eco-activists, peace activists, marketeers, and honest cops—each of them with a light touch, comfort with collaboration, and eagerness to replace themselves with local talent. An example of productive joining of regional business and environmental goals is the Ecotrust project at Willapa Bay, Washington.

By its funding choices and guidelines, Packard Foundation could foster "jointness" in world-saving endeavors. In support of the long now, it could promote people, ideas, and organizations that are in for the long haul.

In his piece "Reframing the Problems," Brand suggests that the first color photographs of the Earth from space sparked the environmental movement. This effect, he says, was an unintended benefit of the U.S. space program. Go online to find those first images of Earth (try this link from NASA: http://nssdc.gsfc.nasa.gov/planetary/lunar/apollo_11_30th.html) or visit the library to find some color images in a print text. Spend some time looking at what you find. What details do you notice? How are the photographs composed? Why do you think these images motivated people to action? What is compelling or persuasive about them?

In "Reframing the Problems," Brand argues for "what a Buddhist engineer might call *right technology*." What exactly does Brand mean by this? After you've established his definition, read "The Geoengineering Gambit" by Kevin Bullis (found on page 173). Do you think the technologies Bullis describes there fit the definition advocated by Brand?

In his interview with *Seed* magazine, Brand makes a distinction between the so called "Greens" and "Turquoises." What is the difference between them? Using resources from the web and from your library, write a short essay in which you distinguish one environmental movement from another. Based on what you've discovered, which approach seems the most useful or perhaps the most necessary to you?

Kevin Bullis is the energy editor for the journal Technology Review, *where this article was published in early 2010. In it, Bullis explains the controversial topic of geoengineering, the use of risky technologies to try to undue some of the damage we have caused the planet.*

THE GEOENGINEERING GAMBIT

For years, radical thinkers have proposed risky technologies that they say could rapidly cool the earth and offset global warming. Now a growing number of mainstream climate scientists say we may have to consider extreme action despite the dangers.

By Kevin Bullis

Rivers fed by melting snow and glaciers supply water to over one-sixth of the world's population—well over a billion people. But these sources of water are quickly disappearing: the Himalayan glaciers that feed rivers in India, China, and other Asian countries could be gone in 25 years. Such effects of climate change no longer surprise scientists. But the speed at which they're happening does. "The earth appears to be changing faster than the climate models predicted," says Daniel Schrag, a professor of earth and planetary sciences at Harvard University, who advises President Obama on climate issues.

Atmospheric levels of carbon dioxide have already climbed to 385 parts per million, well over the 350 parts per million that many scientists say is the upper limit for a relatively stable climate. And despite government-led efforts to limit carbon emissions in many countries, annual emissions from fossil-fuel combustion are going up, not down: over the last two decades, they have increased 41 percent. In the last 10 years, the concentration of carbon dioxide in the atmosphere has increased by nearly two parts per million every year. At this rate, they'll be twice preindustrial levels by the end of the century. Meanwhile, researchers are growing convinced that the climate might be more sensitive to greenhouse gases at this level than once thought. "The likelihood that we're going to avoid serious damage seems quite low," says Schrag. "The best we're going to do is probably not going to be good enough."

This shocking realization has caused many influential scientists, including Obama advisors like Schrag, to fundamentally change their thinking about how to respond to climate change. They have begun calling for the government to start funding research into geoengineering—large-scale schemes for rapidly cooling the earth.

Strategies for geoengineering vary widely, from launching trillions of sun shields into space to triggering vast algae blooms in oceans. The one that has gained the most attention in recent years involves injecting millions of tons of sulfur dioxide high into the atmosphere to form microscopic particles that would shade the planet. Many geoengineering proposals date back decades, but until just a few years ago, most climate scientists considered them something between high-tech hubris and science fiction. Indeed, the subject was "forbidden territory," says Ronald Prinn, a professor of atmospheric sciences at MIT. Not only is it unclear how such engineering feats would be accomplished and whether they would, in fact, moderate the climate, but most scientists worry that they could have disastrous unintended consequences. What's more, relying on geoengineering to cool the earth, rather than cutting greenhouse-gas emissions, would commit future generations to maintaining these schemes indefinitely. For these reasons, mere discussion of geoengineering was considered a dangerous distraction for policy makers considering how to deal with global warming. Prinn says that until a few years ago, he thought its advocates were "off the deep end."

It's not just a fringe idea anymore. The United Kingdom's Royal Society issued a report on geoengineering in September that outlined the research and policy challenges ahead. The National Academies in the United States are working on a similar study. And John Holdren, the director of the White House Office of Science and Technology Policy, broached the idea soon after he was appointed. "Climate change is happening faster than anyone previously predicted," he said during one talk. "If we get sufficiently desperate, we may try to engage in geoengineering to try to create cooling effects." To prepare ourselves, he said, we need to understand the possibilities and the possible side effects. Even the U.S. Congress has now taken an interest, holding its first hearings on geoengineering in November.

Geoengineering might be "a terrible idea," but it might be better than doing nothing, says Schrag. Unlike many past advocates, he doesn't think it's an alternative to reducing greenhouse-gas emissions. "It's not a techno-fix. It's not a Band-Aid. It's a tourniquet," he says. "There are potential side effects, yes. But it may be better than the alternative, which is bleeding to death."

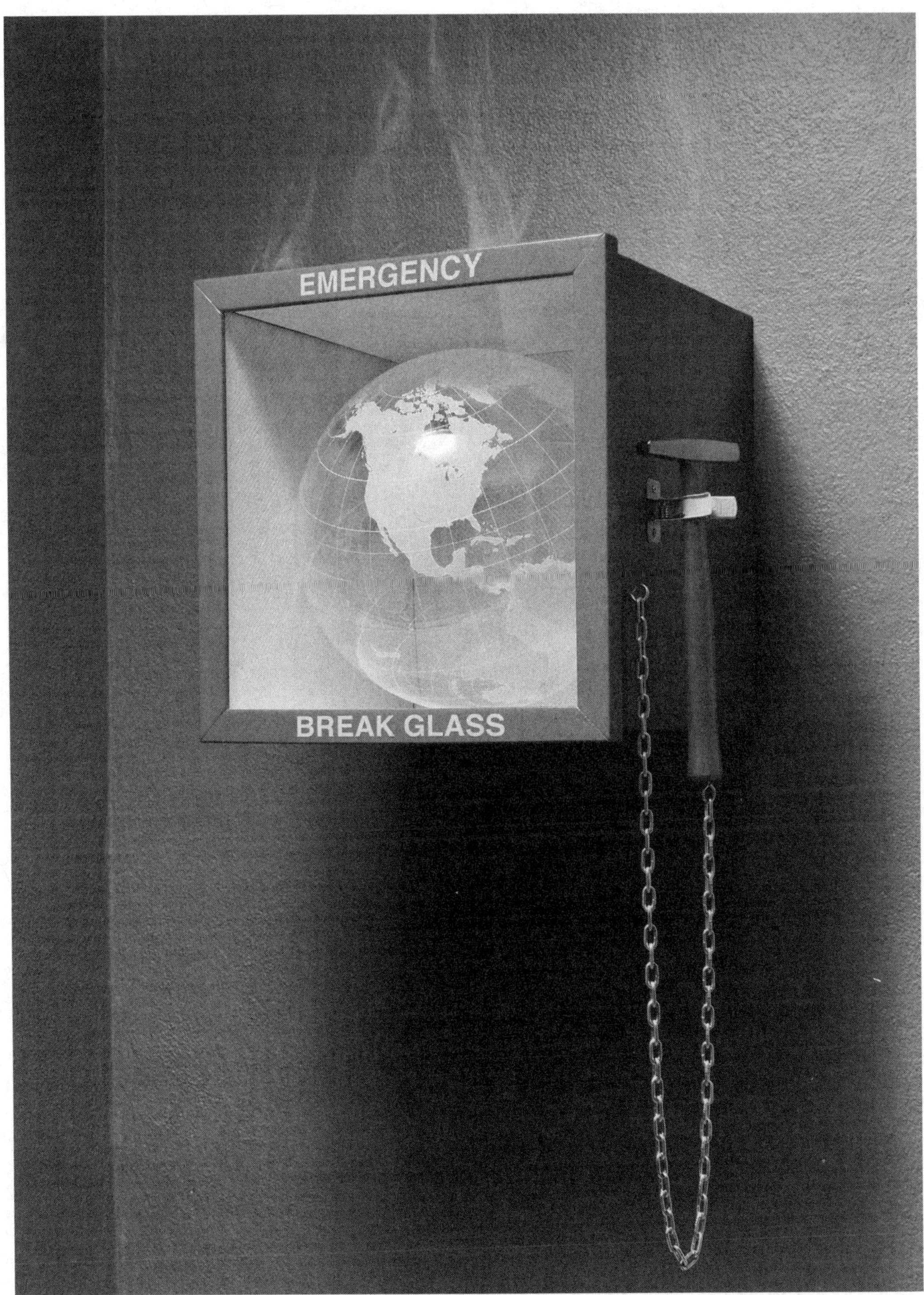

Photograph by Mauricio Alejo

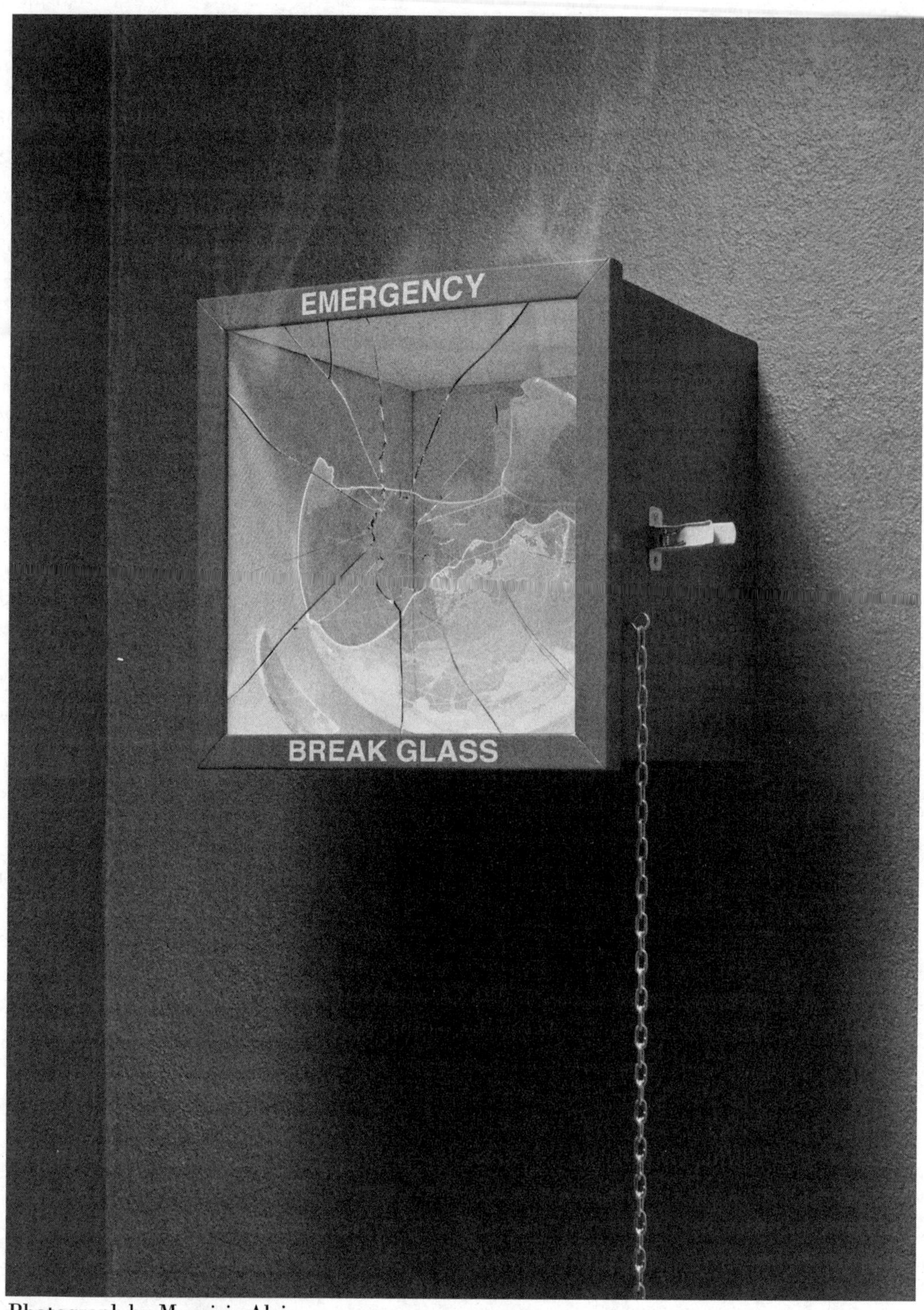

Photograph by Mauricio Alejo

SUNDAY STORMS

The idea of geoengineering has a long history. In the 1830s, James Espy, the first federally funded meteorologist in the United States, wanted to burn large swaths of Appalachian forest every Sunday afternoon, supposing that heat from the fires would induce regular rainstorms. More than a century later, meteorologists and physicists in the United States and the Soviet Union separately considered a range of schemes for changing the climate, often with the goal of warming up northern latitudes to extend growing seasons and clear shipping lanes through the Arctic. In 1974 a Soviet scientist, Mikhail Budyko, first suggested what is today probably the leading plan for cooling down the earth: injecting gases into the upper reaches of the atmosphere, where they would form microscopic particles to block sunlight. The idea is based on a natural phenomenon. Every few decades a volcano erupts so violently that it sends several millions of tons of sulfur—in the form of sulfur dioxide—more than 10 kilometers into the upper reaches of the atmosphere, a region called the stratosphere. The resulting sulfate particles spread out quickly and stay suspended for years. They reflect and diffuse sunlight, creating a haze that whitens blue skies and causes dramatic sunsets. By decreasing the amount of sunlight that reaches the surface, the haze also lowers its temperature. This is what happened after the 1991 eruption of Mount Pinatubo in the Philippines, which released about 15 million tons of sulfur dioxide into the stratosphere. Over the next 15 months, average temperatures dropped by half a degree Celsius. (Within a few years, the sulfates settled out of the stratosphere, and the cooling effect was gone.)

Scientists estimate that compensating for the increase in carbon dioxide levels expected over this century would require pumping between one million and five million tons of sulfur into the stratosphere every year. Diverse strategies for getting all that sulfur up there have been proposed. Billionaire investor Nathan Myhrvold, the former chief technology officer at Microsoft and the founder and CEO of Intellectual Ventures, based in Bellevue, Washington, has thought of several, one of which takes advantage of the fact that coal-fired power plants already emit vast amounts of sulfur dioxide. These emissions stay close to the ground, and rain washes them out of the atmosphere within a couple of weeks. But if the pollution could reach the stratosphere, it would circulate for years, vastly multiplying its impact in reflecting sunlight. To get the sulfur into the stratosphere, Myhrvold suggests, why not use a "flexible, inflatable hot-air-balloon smokestack" 25 kilometers tall? The emissions from just two coal-fired plants might solve the problem, he says. He estimates that his solution would cost less than $100 million a year, including the cost of replacing balloons damaged by storms.

Not surprisingly, climate scientists are not ready to sign off on such a scheme. Some problems are obvious. No one has ever tried to build a 25-kilometer smokestack, for one thing. Moreover, scientists don't understand atmospheric chemistry well enough to be sure what would happen; far from alleviating climate change, shooting tons of sulfates into the stratosphere could have disastrous consequences. The chemistry is too complex for us to be certain, and climate models aren't powerful enough to tell the whole story.

"We know Pinatubo cooled the earth, but that's not the question," Schrag says. "Average temperature is not the only issue." You've also got to account for regional variations in temperature and effects on precipitation, he explains—the very things that climate models are notoriously bad at accounting for. Prinn concurs: "If we lower levels of sunlight, we are unsure of the exact response of the climate system to doing that, for the same reason that we don't know exactly how the climate will respond to a particular level of greenhouse gases." He adds, "That's the big issue. How can you engineer a system you don't fully understand?"

The actual effects of Mount Pinatubo were, in fact, complex. Climate models at the time predicted that by decreasing the amount of sunlight hitting the surface of the earth, the haze of sulfates produced in such an eruption would reduce evaporation, which in turn would lower the amount of precipitation worldwide. Rainfall did decrease—but by much more than scientists had expected. "The year following Mount Pinatubo had by far the lowest amount of rainfall on record," says Kevin Trenberth, a senior scientist at the National Center for Atmospheric Research in Boulder, CO. "In fact, it was 50 percent lower than the previous low of any year." The effects, however, weren't uniform; in some places, precipitation actually increased. A human-engineered sulfate haze could have similarly unpredictable results, scientists warn.

Even in a best-case scenario, where side effects are small and manageable, cooling the planet by deflecting sunlight would not reduce the carbon dioxide in the atmosphere, and elevated levels of that gas have consequences beyond raising the temperature. One is that the ocean absorbs more carbon dioxide and becomes more acidic as a result. That harms shellfish and some forms of plankton, a key source of food for fish and whales. The fishing industry could be devastated. What's more, carbon dioxide levels will continue to rise if we don't address them directly, so any sunlight-reducing technology would have to be continually ratcheted up to compensate for their warming effects.

And if the geoengineering had to stop—say, for environmental or economic reasons—the higher levels of greenhouse gases would cause an abrupt warm-up. "Even if the geoengineering worked perfectly," says Raymond Pierrehumbert, a professor of geophysical sciences at the University of Chicago, "you're still in the situation where the whole planet is just one global war or depression away from being hit with maybe a hundred years' worth of global warming in under a decade, which is certainly catastrophic. Geoengineering, if it were carried out, would put the earth in an extremely precarious state."

SMARTER SULFATES

Figuring out the consequences of various geoengineering plans and developing strategies to make them safer and more effective will take years, or even decades, of research. "For every dollar we spend figuring out how to actually do geoengineering," says Schrag, "we need to be spending 10 dollars learning what the impacts will be."

To begin with, scientists aren't even sure that sulfates delivered over the course of decades, rather than in one short volcanic blast, will work to cool the planet down. One key question is how microscopic particles interact in the stratosphere. It's possible that sulfate particles added repeatedly to the same area over time would clump together. If that happened, the particles could start to interact with longer-wave radiation than just the wavelengths of electromagnetic energy in visible light. This would trap some of the heat that naturally escapes into space, causing a net heating effect rather than a cooling effect. Or the larger particles could fall out of the sky before they had a chance to deflect the sun's heat. To study such phenomena, David Keith, the director of the Energy and Environmental Systems Group at the University of Calgary, envisions experiments in which a plane would spray a gas at low vapor pressure over an area of 100 square kilometers. The gas would condense into particles in the stratosphere, and the plane would fly back through the particle cloud to take measurements. Systematically altering the size of the particles, the quantity of particles in a given area, the timing of their release, and other variables could reveal key details about their microscale interactions.

Yet even if the behavior of sulfate particles can be understood and managed, it's far from clear how injecting them into the stratosphere would affect vast, complex climate systems. So far, most models have been crude; only recently, for example, did they start taking into account the movement of ice and ocean currents. Sulfates would cool the planet during the day, but they'd make no difference when the sun isn't shining. As a result, nights would probably be warmer relative to days, but scientists have done little to model this effect and study how it could affect ecosystems. "Similarly, you could affect the seasons," Schrag says: the sulfates would lower temperatures less during the winter (when there's less daylight) and more during the summer. And scientists have done little to understand how stratospheric circulation patterns would change with the addition of sulfates, or precisely how any of these things could affect where and when we might experience droughts, floods, and other disasters.

If scientists could learn more about the effects of sulfates in the stratosphere, it could raise the intriguing possibility of "smart" geoengineering, Schrag says. Volcanic eruptions are crude tools, releasing a lot of sulfur in the course of a few days, and all from one location. But geoengineers could choose exactly where to send sulfates into the stratosphere, as well as when and how fast.

"So far we're thinking about a very simplistic thing," Schrag says. "We're talking about injecting stuff in the stratosphere in a uniform way." The effects that have been predicted so far, however, aren't evenly distributed. Changes in evaporation, for example, could be devastating if they caused droughts on land, but if less rain falls over the ocean, it's not such a big deal. By taking advantage of stratospheric circulation patterns and seasonal variations in weather, it might be possible to limit the most damaging consequences. "You can pulse injections," he says. "You could build smart systems that might cancel out some of those negative effects."

Rather than intentionally polluting the stratosphere, a different and potentially less risky approach to geoengineering is to pull carbon dioxide out of the air. But the necessary technology would be challenging to develop and put in place on large scale.

In his 10th-floor lab in the Manhattan neighborhood of Morningside Heights, Klaus Lackner, a professor of geophysics in the Department of Earth and Environmental Engineering at Columbia University, is experimenting with a material that chemically binds to carbon dioxide in the air and then, when doused in water, releases the gas in a concentrated form that can easily be captured. The

FIVE GEOENGINEERING SCHEMES

Researchers and entrepreneurs have proposed approaches ranging from the relatively cheap and simple to the elaborate. Here are the ones that have received the most attention so far.

SULFATE INJECTION

Aircraft, or a hose suspended by hundreds of wing-shaped balloons, could inject aerosols into the upper atmosphere. The particles would reflect light and shade the earth.
Pros: It could be cheap and fast-acting, cooling the earth in months.
Cons: It could cause droughts. Injections might need to continue for hundreds of years.

CLOUD BRIGHTENING

Tiny droplets made by spraying an extremely fine mist of seawater into low-lying clouds could make them reflect more sunlight than ordinary clouds.
Pros: Shading could be targeted—to stop the melting of Arctic Sea ice, for example.
Cons: Scientists don't know how it would affect precipitation and temperatures over land, where it would matter most.

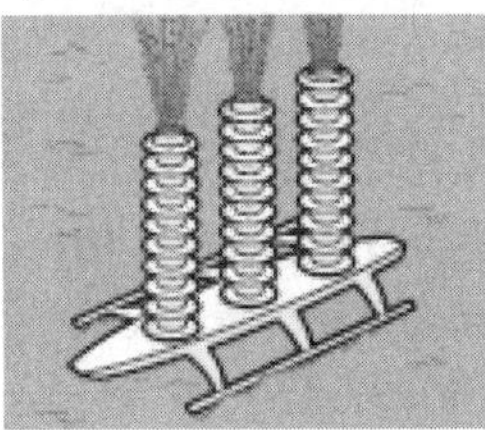

OCEAN FERTILIZATION

Adding iron or other nutrients to the ocean could promote algae blooms, which would capture carbon dioxide and store some of it deep in the ocean.
Pros: It would directly address the root of climate change: carbon dioxide in the atmosphere.
Cons: At best, it could offset an eighth of the greenhouse-gas emissions attributed to humans, and it could harm ecosystems.

SPACE SHADES

Trillions of disks launched into space could reflect incoming sunlight.
Pros: Space-based systems don't pollute the atmosphere. Once in place, they would cool the earth quickly.
Cons: The technology could take decades to develop. And launching trillions of disks is fantastically expensive.

ARTIFICIAL TREES

Various chemical reactions can be used to capture carbon dioxide from the atmosphere for permanent storage.
Pros: In the long run, this could reduce atmospheric concentrations of carbon dioxide. There is no obvious limit to how much of the greenhouse gas could be stored.
Cons: It could be very expensive and energy intensive, and it would take a long time to reduce temperatures.

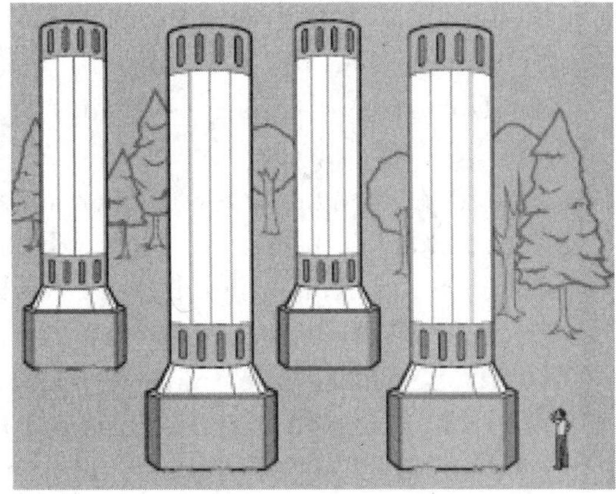

work is at an early stage. Lackner's carbon-capture devices look like misshapen test-tube brushes; they have to be hand dipped in water, and it's hard to quickly seal them into the improvised chamber used to measure the carbon dioxide they release. But he envisions automated systems—millions of them, each the size of a small cabin—scattered over the countryside near geologic reservoirs that could store the gases they capture. A system based on this material, he calculates, could remove carbon dioxide from the air a thousand times as fast as trees do now. Others at Columbia are working on ways to exploit the fact that peridotite rock reacts with carbon dioxide to form magnesium carbonate and other minerals, removing the greenhouse gas from the atmosphere. The researchers hope to speed up these natural reactions.

It's far from clear that these ideas for capturing carbon will be practical. Some may even require so much energy that they create a net increase in carbon dioxide. "But even if it takes us a hundred years to learn how to do it," Pierrehumbert says, "it's still useful, because CO_2 naturally takes a thousand years to get out of the atmosphere."

THE SEEDS OF WAR

Several existing geoengineering schemes, though, could be attempted relatively cheaply and easily. And even if no one knows whether they would be safe or effective, that doesn't mean they won't be tried.

David Victor, the director of the Laboratory on International Law and Regulation at the University of California, San Diego, sees two scenarios in which it might happen. First, "the desperate Hail Mary pass:" "A country quite vulnerable to changing climate is desperate to alter outcomes and sees that efforts to cut emissions are not bearing fruit. Crude geoengineering schemes could be very inexpensive, and thus this option might even be available to a Trinidad or Bangladesh—the former rich in gas exports and quite vulnerable, and the latter poor but large enough that it might do something seen as essential for survival." And second, "the Soviet-style arrogant engineering scenario:" "A country run by engineers and not overly exposed to public opinion or to dissenting voices undertakes geoengineering as a national mission—much like massive building of poorly designed nuclear reactors, river diversion projects, resettlement of populations, and other national missions that are hard to pursue when the public is informed, responsive, and in power." In either case, a single country acting alone could influence the climate of the entire world.

How would the world react? In extreme cases, Victor says, it could lead to war. Some countries might object to cooling the earth, especially if higher temperatures have brought them advantages such as longer growing seasons and milder winters. And if geoengineering decreases rainfall, countries that have experienced droughts due to global warming could suffer even more.

No current international laws or agreements would clearly prevent a country from unilaterally starting a geoengineering project. And too little is known now for a governing body such as the United Nations to establish sound regulations—regulations that might in any case be ignored by a country set on trying to save itself from a climate disaster. Victor says the best hope is for leading scientists around the world to collaborate on establishing as clearly as possible what dangers could be involved in geoengineering and how, if at all, it might be used. Through open international research, he says, we can "increase the odds—not to 100 percent—that responsible norms would emerge."

READY OR NOT

In 2006, Paul Crutzen, the Dutch scientist who won the Nobel Prize in chemistry for his discoveries about the depletion of the stratospheric ozone layer, wrote an essay in the journal *Climatic Change* in which he declared that efforts to reduce greenhouse-gas emissions "have been grossly unsuccessful." He called for increased research into the "feasibility and environmental consequences of climate engineering," even though he acknowledged that injecting sulfates into the stratosphere could damage the ozone layer and cause large, unpredictable side effects. Despite these dangers, he said, climatic engineering could ultimately be "the only option available to rapidly reduce temperature rises."

At the time, Crutzen's essay was controversial, and many scientists called it irresponsible. But since then it has served to bring geoengineering into the open, says David Keith, who started studying the subject in 1989. After a scientist of Crutzen's credentials, who understood the stratosphere as well as anyone, came out in favor of studying sulfate injection as a way to cool the earth, many other scientists were willing to start talking about it.

Among the most recent converts is David Battisti, a professor of atmospheric sciences at the University of Washington. One problem in particular worries him. Studies of heat waves show that crop yields drop off sharply when temperatures rise 3 °C to 4 °C above normal—the temperatures that MIT's Prinn predicts we might reach even with strict emissions controls. Speaking at a geoengineering symposium at MIT this fall, Battisti said, "By the end of the century, just due to temperature alone, we're looking at a 30 to 40 percent reduction in [crop] yields, while in the next 50 years demand for food is expected to more than double."

Battisti is well aware of the uncertainties that surround geoengineering. According to research he's conducted recently, the first computer models that tried to show how shading the earth would affect climate were off by 2 °C to 3 °C in predictions of regional temperature change and by as much as 40 percent in predictions of regional rainfall. But with a billion people already malnourished, and billions more who could go hungry if global warming disrupts agriculture, Battisti has reluctantly conceded that we may need to consider "a climate-engineering patch." Better data and better models will help clarify the effects of geoengineering. "Give us 30 or 40 years and we'll be there," he said at the MIT symposium. "But in 30 to 40 years, at the level we're increasing CO_2, we're going to need this, whether we're ready or not."

In his article, Bullis writes, "Many geoengineering proposals date back decades, but until just a few years ago, most climate scientists considered them something between high-tech hubris and science fiction." Why, according to Bullis, have these proposals been pushed to the fringes for so long? What has changed in recent years to bring geoengineering into more acceptable scientific and political discussions? What do you think the future holds for these approaches to dealing with climate change?

Among journalists, scientists, and policymakers, the critical question surrounding geoengineering is not, "How we would do it?" but rather, "Should we do it?" Write a short essay in which you characterize the ethical dilemmas attached to geoengineering. Write your own responses to these dilemmas. If we had the technology to cool the planet through geoengineering, should we do it? Why or why not?

Writer, speaker, and teacher Courtney E. Martin wrote this article in May 2010 for the online edition of The American Prospect, *where she is a senior correspondent. She is the author of* Perfect Girls, Starving Daughters: The Frightening New Normalcy of Hating Your Body *and, most recently, of* Do It Now: The New Generation of Activists.

THE POPULATION DEBATE GETS PERSONAL

BY COURTNEY E. MARTIN

Let's be honest, babies aren't known for being camera shy, but they've really been hogging the spotlight as of late. There's that new Focus Features film, *Babies*. And then last week *The New York Times Sunday Magazine* explored their morality in a cover story chock-full of images of cartoonishly big-eyed infants.

But don't be fooled by their innocent appearance. While fertility rates have been consistently dropping worldwide over the last 10 years, we're still way over budget when it comes to those chubby little humans. Last year, according to the Global Footprint Network, 6.8 billion of us consumed the renewable resources of 1.4 Earths.

Gustav Vigeland's sculpture "Swarm of Babies," in the Vigeland Sculpture Park, Oslo, Norway.

Overpopulation is a controversial topic for a slew of reasons, not the least of which is that those who've taken up the cause have often been racist, classist, xenophobic, and sexist. I won't belabor the history here; *Mother Jones*' recent cover story, "The Last Taboo," and

"The Last Taboo"

related online forum (of which I was a part) are good places to find a more comprehensive background.

But another, less discussed reason that conversations about overpopulation are so explosive is that they're inherently very personal. This topic is one of the most extreme reminders that some of our most private decisions have real and lasting public consequences. Even when a Prius-driving, bottle-recycling, Sierra Club-donating woman is deciding whether to have a baby, she is rarely focused on the environmental consequences, and yet, an American baby born today adds an average of 10,407 tons of carbon dioxide to the carbon legacy of the mother—according to Oregon State University statistician Paul Murtaugh.

This kind of personal-political dynamic is different than individual moralizing or religious values. This is not the stuff of the culture wars—Is it wrong to have an abortion? Is it right to censor sexually explicit art? These are, ultimately, questions that are interpretable and value-driven, the stuff of philosophy classes and religious sermons. My yes may be just as defendable as your no.

The question of overpopulation is different. While one may quibble with Murtaugh's calculations, one can't really argue that it's environmentally sound to birth another child into our resource-depleted Earth. In fact, author Bill McKibben argues that we've changed the quality of the planet so drastically that we can't even call it Earth anymore. We're now living on Eaarth, as he calls it in his latest book, *Making Life on a Tough New Planet*, and our job is to figure out how to not screw this one up, too.

Of course there are big-picture, non-coercive solutions to overpopulation. Improve girls' education, and fertility rates automatically drop (an approach dubbed "the girl effect"). Make sure that contraception is cheap, abundant, and culturally acceptable. Give women economic opportunities. These are libratory, First World answers to Third World problems. Educate a girl and, voila, the world is saved!

But what about Americans? As of 2005, women in 18 of the 24 wealthiest nations were having more babies than in previous years. No one has posited any big theories on why this trend has reversed in countries where women are largely well educated, the U.S. included, but there's no question that babies born in wealthy countries consume a disproportionate amount of resources.

So where do we draw the line in our own procreating and consuming habits? No self-respecting environmentalist drinks out of disposable plastic water bottles, but does she unapologetically have a few kiddos? Murtaugh told *Mother Jones* environmental correspondent Julia Whitty: "The ecological costs of that child far outweigh even the combined energy-saving choices from all a mother's other good decisions, like buying a fuel-efficient car, recycling, using energy-saving appliances and light bulbs. The carbon legacy of one American child and her offspring is 20 times greater than all those other sustainable maternal choices combined."

I haven't yet been faced with the ecological realities of my own capacity to procreate, but I can only imagine that the prospect of co-parenting, funding diapers and a college education, and losing my long, lazy Sunday mornings will loom far larger in my mind than Murtaugh's calculations. Perhaps this is the inevitable selfishness of human nature, or maybe I—like so many privileged Americans—let myself off the moral hook too easily.

I've already made smaller-scale versions of this calculation. I've held off on buying a new iPhone, for example, until my old BlackBerry dies. Part of this is thrift, but part of it is also a general environmental value—I try not to replace anything that isn't irreparably broken. When I make this decision, I don't imagine the trash pickers of Rio hiking over the discarded whims of wealthy folks, but I do have a general sense that I'm making a choice that's better for my budget and better for everyone else, too.

An iPhone, as coveted as it may be, is not a baby. I get it. But in terms of personal choice, consumption, and global interdependence, the two are on a relevant continuum. Americans, most of them anyway, live in a time of relative abundance, even in this economic recession. We are faced with daily choices that impact the rest of the world in very concrete ways, and this new reality requires what Daniel Goleman calls "ecological intelligence"—the capacity to analyze what we consume so as to make the most sustainable decision.

Thus far, consuming via baby-making has been a no-judgment zone for most Americans, even the most "green" among us. Babies sure are cute. And creating a family is a complex, highly personal art. Many mothers I know say that having a child is the most miraculous experience they've ever had. Turns out, harsh as it sounds, that it's also one of the most environmentally irresponsible.

It's easy to understand why we don't weigh these public ramifications in our procreation decisions, but it doesn't make it right.

In the introduction to "The Population Debate Gets Personal," Martin refers to a May/June 2010 article ("The Last Taboo" by Julia Whitty) in *Mother Jones* about overpopulation and the environment. Read this piece (here's a link to the essay: http://motherjones.com/environment/2010/05/population-growth-india-vatican) and summarize the politically touchy issues to which Martin refers. How does knowing this background contextualize Martin's essay?

Martin's essay introduces a different—and perhaps surprising—way of thinking about the effects our reproductive choices have on the environment. Identify her main argument, and consider her claims. Does she change the way you think about the consequences of having children?

Journalist and author Alan Weisman's work has appeared in publications around the world. This piece, from the February 2005 edition of Discover *magazine, foreshadowed Weisman's 2007 book* The World Without Us. *Weisman's project here is to show the effects humans have on the planet by speculating about what the world would be like without us.*

EARTH WITHOUT PEOPLE

BY ALAN WEISMAN

Given the mounting toll of fouled oceans, overheated air, missing topsoil, and mass extinctions, we might sometimes wonder what our planet would be like if humans suddenly disappeared. Would Superfund sites revert to Gardens of Eden? Would the seas again fill with fish? Would our concrete cities crumble to dust from the force of tree roots, water, and weeds? How long would it take for our traces to vanish? And if we could answer such questions, would we be more in awe of the changes we have wrought, or of nature's resilience?

A good place to start searching for answers is in Korea, in the 155-mile-long, 2.5-mile-wide mountainous Demilitarized Zone, or DMZ, set up by the armistice ending the Korean War. Aside from rare military patrols or desperate souls fleeing North Korea, humans have barely set foot in the strip since 1953. Before that, for 5,000 years, the area was populated by rice farmers who carved the land into paddies. Today those paddies have become barely discernible, transformed into pockets of marsh, and the new occupants of these lands arrive as dazzling white squadrons of red-crowned cranes that glide over the bulrushes in perfect formation, touching down so lightly that they detonate no land mines. Next to whooping cranes, they are the rarest such birds on Earth. They winter in the DMZ alongside the endangered white-naped cranes, revered in Asia as sacred portents of peace.

If peace is ever declared, suburban Seoul, which has rolled ever northward in recent decades, is poised to invade such tantalizing real estate. On the other side, the North Koreans are building an industrial megapark. This has spurred an international coalition of scientists called the DMZ Forum to try to consecrate the area for a peace park and nature preserve. Imagine it as "a Korean Gettysburg and Yosemite rolled together," says Harvard University biologist Edward O. Wilson, who believes that tourism revenues could trump those from agriculture or development.

As serenely natural as the DMZ now is, it would be far different if people throughout Korea suddenly disappeared. The habitat would not revert to a truly natural state until the dams that now divert rivers to slake the needs of Seoul's more than 20 million inhabitants failed—a century or two after the humans had gone. But in the meantime, says Wilson, many creatures would flourish. Otters, Asiatic black bears, musk deer, and the nearly vanquished Amur leopard would spread into slopes reforested with young daimyo oak and bird cherry. The few Siberian tigers that still prowl the North Korean-Chinese borderlands would multiply and fan across Asia's temperate zones. "The wild carnivores would make short work of livestock," he says. "Few domestic animals would remain after a couple of hundred years. Dogs would go feral, but they wouldn't last long: They'd never be able to compete."

If people were no longer present anywhere on Earth, a worldwide shakeout would follow. From zebra mussels to fire ants to crops to kudzu, exotics would battle with natives. In time, says Wilson, all human attempts to improve on nature, such as our painstakingly bred horses, would revert to their origins. If horses survived at all, they would devolve back to Przewalski's horse, the only true wild horse, still found in the Mongolian steppes. "The plants, crops, and animal species man has wrought by his own hand would be wiped out in a century or two," Wilson says. In a few thousand years, "the world would mostly look as it did before humanity came along—like a wilderness."

The new wilderness would consume cities, much as the jungle of northern Guatemala consumed the Mayan pyramids and megalopolises of overlapping city-states. From A.D. 800 to 900, a combination of drought and internecine warfare over dwindling farmland brought 2,000 years of civilization crashing down. Within 10 centuries, the jungle swallowed all.

Mayan communities alternated urban living with fields sheltered by forests, in contrast with today's paved cities, which are more like man-made deserts. However, it wouldn't take long for nature to undo even the likes of a New York

In many cities, streets would turn quickly into waterways.

City. Jameel Ahmad, civil engineering department chair at Cooper Union College in New York City, says repeated freezing and thawing common in months like March and November would split cement within a decade, allowing water to seep in. As it, too, froze and expanded, cracks would widen. Soon, weeds such as mustard and goosegrass would invade. With nobody to trample seedlings, New York's prolific exotic, the Chinese ailanthus tree, would take over. Within five years, says Dennis Stevenson, senior curator at the New York Botanical Garden, ailanthus roots would heave up sidewalks and split sewers.

That would exacerbate a problem that already plagues New York—rising groundwater. There's little soil to absorb it or vegetation to transpire it, and buildings block the sunlight that could evaporate it. With the power off, pumps that keep subways from flooding would be stilled. As water sluiced away soil beneath pavement, streets would crater.

Eric Sanderson of the Bronx Zoo Wildlife Conservation Society heads the Mannahatta Project, a virtual re-creation of pre-1609 Manhattan. He says there were 30 to 40 streams in Manhattan when the Dutch first arrived. If New Yorkers disappeared, sewers would clog, some natural watercourses would reappear, and others would form. Within 20 years, the water-soaked steel columns that support the street above the East Side's subway tunnels would corrode and buckle, turning Lexington Avenue into a river.

New York's architecture isn't as flammable as San Francisco's clapboard Victorians, but within 200 years, says Steven Clemants, vice president of the Brooklyn Botanic Garden, tons of leaf litter would overflow gutters as pioneer weeds gave way to colonizing native oaks and maples in city parks. A dry lightning strike, igniting decades of uncut, knee-high Central Park grass, would spread flames through town.

As lightning rods rusted away, roof fires would leap among buildings into paneled offices filled with paper. Meanwhile, native Virginia creeper and poison ivy would claw at walls covered with lichens, which thrive in the absence of air pollution. Wherever foundations failed and buildings tumbled, lime from crushed concrete would raise soil pH, inviting buckthorn and birch. Black locust and autumn olive trees would fix nitrogen, allowing more goldenrods, sunflowers, and white snakeroot to move in along with apple trees, their seeds expelled by proliferating birds. Sweet carrots would quickly devolve to their wild form, unpalatable Queen Anne's lace, while broccoli, cabbage, brussels sprouts, and cauliflower would regress to the same unrecognizable broccoli ancestor.

Unless an earthquake strikes New York first, bridges spared yearly applications of road salt would last a few hundred years before their stays and bolts gave way (last to fall would be Hell Gate Arch, built for railroads and easily good for another thousand years). Coyotes would invade Central Park, and deer, bears, and finally wolves would follow. Ruins would echo the love song of frogs breeding in streams stocked with alewives, herring, and mussels dropped by seagulls. Missing, however, would be all fauna that have adapted to humans. The invincible cockroach, an insect that originated in the hot climes of Africa, would succumb in unheated buildings. Without garbage, rats would starve or serve as lunch for peregrine falcons and red-tailed hawks. Pigeons would genetically revert back to the rock doves from which they sprang.

It's unclear how long animals would suffer from the urban legacy of concentrated heavy metals. Over many centuries, plants would take these up, recycle, redeposit, and gradually dilute them. The time bombs left in petroleum tanks, chemical plants, power plants, and dry-cleaning plants might poison the earth beneath them for eons. One intriguing example is the former Rocky Mountain Arsenal next to Denver International Airport. There a chemical weapons plant produced mustard and nerve gas, incendiary bombs, napalm, and after World War II, pesticides. In 1984 it was considered by the arsenal commander to be the most contaminated spot in the United States. Today it is a national wildlife refuge, home to bald eagles that feast on its prodigious prairie dog population.

However, it took more than $130 million and a lot of man-hours to drain and seal the arsenal's lake, in which ducks once died minutes after landing and the aluminum bottoms of boats sent to fetch their carcasses rotted within a month. In a world with no one left to bury the bad stuff, decaying chemical containers would slowly expose their lethal contents. Places like the Indian Point nuclear power plant, 35 miles north of Times Square, would dump radioactivity into the Hudson long after the lights went out.

Old stone buildings in Manhattan, such as Grand Central Station or the Metropolitan Museum of Art, would outlast every modern glass box, especially with no more acid rain to pock their marble. Still, at some point thousands of years hence, the last stone walls—perhaps chunks of St. Paul's Chapel on Wall Street, built in 1766 from Manhattan's own hard schist—would fall. Three times in the past 100,000 years, glaciers have scraped New York clean, and they'll do so again. The mature hardwood forest would be mowed down. On Staten Island, Fresh Kills's four giant mounds of trash would be flattened, their vast accumulation of stubborn PVC plastic and glass ground to powder. After the ice receded, an unnatural concentration of reddish metal—remnants of wiring and plumbing—would remain buried in layers. The next toolmaker to arrive or evolve might discover it and use it, but there would be nothing to indicate who had put it there.

Before humans appeared, an oriole could fly from the Mississippi to the Atlantic and never alight on anything other than a treetop. Unbroken forest blanketed Europe from the Urals to the English Channel. The last remaining fragment of that primeval European wilderness—half a million acres of woods straddling the border between Poland and Belarus, called the Bialowieza Forest—provides another glimpse of how the world would look if we were gone. There, relic groves of huge ash and linden trees rise 138 feet above an understory of hornbeams, ferns, swamp alders, massive birches, and crockery-size fungi. Norway spruces, shaggy as Methuselah, stand even taller. Five-century-old oaks grow so immense that great spotted woodpeckers stuff whole spruce cones in their three-inch-deep bark furrows. The woods carry pygmy owl whistles, nutcracker croaks, and wolf howls. Fragrance wafts from eons of mulch.

High privilege accounts for such unbroken antiquity. During the 14th century, a Lithuanian duke declared it a royal hunting preserve. For centuries it stayed that way. Eventually, the forest was subsumed by Russia and in 1888 became the private domain of the czars. Occupying Germans took lumber and slaughtered game during World War I, but a pristine core was left intact, which in 1921 became a Polish national park. Timber pillaging resumed briefly under the

Soviets, but when the Nazis invaded, nature fanatic Hermann Göring decreed the entire preserve off limits. Then, following World War II, a reportedly drunken Josef Stalin agreed one evening in Warsaw to let Poland retain two-fifths of the forest.

To realize that all of Europe once looked like this is startling. Most unexpected of all is the sight of native bison. Just 600 remain in the wild, on both sides of an impassable iron curtain erected by the Soviets in 1980 along the border to thwart escapees to Poland's renegade Solidarity movement. Although wolves dig under it, and roe deer are believed to leap over it, the herd of the largest of Europe's mammals remains divided, and thus its gene pool. Belarus, which has not removed its statues of Lenin, has no specific plans to dismantle the fence. Unless it does, the bison may suffer genetic degradation, leaving them vulnerable to a disease that would wipe them out.

If the bison herd withers, they would join all the other extinct megafauna that even our total disappearance could never bring back. In a glass case in his laboratory, paleoecologist Paul S. Martin at the University of Arizona keeps a lump of dried dung he found in a Grand Canyon cave, left by a sloth weighing 200 pounds. That would have made it the smallest of several North American ground sloth species present when humans first appeared on this continent. The largest was as big as an elephant and lumbered around by the thousands in the woodlands and deserts of today's United States. What we call pristine today, Martin says, is a poor reflection of what would be here if Homo sapiens had never evolved.

"America would have three times as many species of animals over 1,000 pounds as Africa does today," he says. An amazing megafaunal menagerie roamed the region: Giant armadillos resembling armor-plated autos; bears twice the size of grizzlies; the hoofed, herbivorous toxodon, big as a rhinoceros; and saber-toothed tigers. A dozen species of horses were here, as well as the camel-like litoptern, giant beavers, giant peccaries, woolly rhinos, mammoths, and mastodons. Climate change and imported disease may have killed them, but most paleontologists accept the theory Martin advocates: "When people got out of Africa and Asia and reached other parts of the world, all hell broke loose." He is convinced that people were responsible for the mass extinctions because they commenced with human arrival everywhere: first, in Australia 60,000 years ago, then mainland America 13,000 years ago, followed by the Caribbean islands 6,000 years ago, and Madagascar 2,000 years ago.

Yet one place on Earth did manage to elude the intercontinental holocaust: the oceans. Dolphins and whales escaped for the simple reason that prehistoric people could not hunt enough giant marine mammals to have a major impact on the population. "At least a dozen species in the ocean Columbus sailed were bigger than his biggest ship," says marine paleoecologist Jeremy Jackson of the Smithsonian Tropical Research Institute in Panama. "Not only mammals—the sea off Cuba was so thick with 1,000-pound green turtles that his boats practically ran aground on them." This was a world where ships collided with schools of whales and where sharks were so abundant they would swim up rivers to prey on cattle. Reefs swarmed with 800-pound goliath grouper, not just today's puny aquarium species. Cod could be fished from the sea in baskets. Oysters filtered all the water in Chesapeake Bay every five days. The planet's shores teemed with millions of manatees, seals, and walrus.

Within the past century, however, humans have flattened the coral reefs on the continental shelves and scraped the sea grass beds bare; a dead zone bigger than New Jersey grows at the mouth of the Mississippi; all the world's cod fisheries have collapsed. What Pleistocene humans did in 1,500 years to terrestrial life, modern man has done in mere decades to the oceans—"almost," Jackson says. Despite mechanized overharvesting, satellite fish tracking, and prolonged butchery of sea mammals, the ocean is still bigger than we are. "It's not like the land," he says. "The great majority of sea species are badly depleted, but they still exist. If people actually went away, most could recover."

Even if global warming or ultraviolet radiation bleaches the Great Barrier Reef to death, Jackson says, "it's only 7,000 years old. New reefs have had to form before. It's not like the world is a constant place." Without people, most excess industrial carbon dioxide would dissipate within 200 years, cooling the atmosphere. With no further chlorine and bromine leaking skyward, within decades the ozone layer would replenish, and ultraviolet damage would subside. Eventually, heavy metals and toxins would flush through the system; a few intractable PCBs might take a millennium.

During that same span, every dam on Earth would silt up and spill over. Rivers would again carry nutrients seaward, where most life would be, as it was long before vertebrates crawled onto the shore. Eventually, that would happen again. The world would start over.

"Earth without People" is a speculative causal argument in which Weisman considers what would happen to the Earth if the human species were to disappear. What does Weisman think would happen without us? What deeper argument about humans and our relation to the Earth does he imply in his essay?

After reading "Earth Without People," watch comedic great George Carlin's classic bit "The Planet is Fine" from his 1992 show *Jammin' in New York* (you can find a video clip here: http://www.youtube.com/watch?v=EjmtSkl53h4). Write a short essay in which you compare the implicit arguments of Weisman and Carlin. What do they have in common? What are the limits of stand-up for presenting an argument about the effects of humans on the fate of the planet? What are the benefits?

MAJOR ASSIGNMENTS

MAJOR ASSIGNMENT #1: WRITING AN ENVIRONMENTAL MEMOIR

BACKGROUND

In "Ecology of a Cracker Childhood" (page 27), Janisse Ray describes the powerful influence that the rural south Georgia landscape—with its beautiful longleaf pines—had on her life. She connects her vivid experiences as a child in the pine flatwoods to her identity, making the practice of clear-cutting the forests an inherently personal affair.

ASSIGNMENT

With a few of Ray's strategies in mind, write an environmental memoir that uses thoughtful plotting, vivid description, and character development to tell a compelling narrative about one significant environmental moment, memory, or theme that is drawn from your life. Base your memoir on an experience that left a lasting impression on you and that you can use to speak to your audience.

QUESTIONS FOR INVENTION

After you have decided on your topic, think about the following questions:

- What specific message do you want to convey about your environment-related experience? (In other words, what is your purpose in writing about this particular place?)

- What kind of reaction do you want from your audience? What do you want them to take from your essay?
- What is the best way to connect with your audience? (Think, for example, about the things you want your audience to see, hear, smell, and feel about your subject.)

ABOUT MEMOIR ESSAYS

A memoir is a kind of personal essay in which the writer uses selected life experiences to connect with and convey a larger message to the audience. As you brainstorm and begin drafting your essay, keep in mind that a memoir should:

- Focus on a slice of your life, rather than your entire life, to convey a specific message and/or emotion to the audience.
- Explore your memory of the experience, using narratives, in order to explain its significance to the audience.
- Include concrete details that appeal to the audience's senses.
- Reflect on the experience to help the audience understand how it affected you and why it should matter to them.

MAJOR ASSIGNMENT #2: ANALYZING COVERAGE OF A GREEN ISSUE

BACKGROUND

Environmental issues, like just about anything else that stirs emotions and debate, are reported on and written about in vastly different ways online, on television and radio, and in print. Why? Because the sources of that coverage—be they bloggers, news media, businesses, special interest groups, or others—tailor their coverage to appeal to their audiences and to achieve specific purposes. Think, for a moment, about how Mike Tidwell's column "To Really Save the Planet, Stop Going Green" (page 113) challenges some of the core ideas in Colin Beavan's "Life after the Year without Toilet Paper" (page 99) and Christie Matheson's *Green Chic: Saving the Earth in Style* (page 83). While writing from a similar ideological position as Beavan and Matheson, Tidwell presents his argument with a specific audience and purpose in mind—these rhetorical concerns, in other words, shape his piece.

ASSIGNMENT

Write an essay in which you analyze and compare the ways that two media websites have covered (or are covering) the same environmental issue or development. Please note that this is not a traditional compare-and-contrast assignment in which you simply report the surface similarities and differences between two subjects. Your focus should be on analyzing the rhetorical choices the two web sources make as they try to inform, move, and persuade their audiences. Some of the choices will be similar and others different. You should make note of that and also explain how and why these differences matter, based on the purpose of each website.

CHOOSING A TOPIC

You could get started on this project in one of two ways: You might select an environmental issue or development that interests you (destruction of the Guatemalan rain forests, for example) and then find two websites that take different approaches to the topic. Or, you might go immediately to two web sources that you know have very different agendas (such as Greenpeace and

Fox News) and then examine their coverage of specific environmental issues. One timely choice for this assignment is the environmental disaster in the Gulf of Mexico brought on by the Deepwater Horizon explosion and subsequent oil leak. Just about every entity with a stake in the disaster has a web presence, and many of these have covered the developments in very different ways. But there are many other interesting and relevant options out there, so you might want to spend a bit of time doing online research before settling on a topic.

INVENTION QUESTIONS

These questions are designed to help you prepare to draft your essay. You should consider the questions for each website separately before you begin your comparison:

QUESTIONS ABOUT YOUR SUBJECT

- What is the name of the website? What kind of website is it? (Is it a news media website? An advocacy site? Or something else?)
- Who is the target audience?

QUESTIONS ABOUT CONTENT

- How much and what kinds of written texts does the site include (news articles, opinion columns, informational pieces, others)?
- Describe the images on the site (Are there photos? Informational graphics? Videos? What do they show?)
- Does the site include advertising? What kinds of ads? Whom do the ads seem to target?
- Who are the stakeholders in the issue? How are their interests represented?
- Is there anything else noteworthy about the content?

QUESTIONS ABOUT TONE

- How would you describe the tone of the website? Is it trying to be objective? Does it have an obvious agenda? (If so, what is that agenda?) Is it angry (or does it convey some other emotion)? Is it trying to be helpful and informative?
- How does the website achieve its tone? (Through the language it uses? Or images? Or something else?)

QUESTIONS ABOUT RHETORICAL CHOICES

- Does the site make any emotional appeals to the audience? (Does it do anything to make the audience feel a certain way?) Are these effective?
- Does the site make any intellectual appeals to the audience? (Does it provide evidence to support its positions? Or does it offer data, statistics, or expertise about the issue at hand?) Are these effective?
- How does the organization behind the website present itself?

QUESTIONS ABOUT PURPOSE

- What do you think the website's purpose is? (What is it trying to do for or to its target audience?)
- Does the website achieve its purpose? If so, how? If not, why not?

MAJOR ASSIGNMENT #3: EXPLAINING A GREEN TECHNOLOGY

BACKGROUND

"The Geoengineering Gambit" by Kevin Bullis (page 173) engages in explanatory writing—that is, it introduces and explains information and ideas with which the audience may not be familiar. Explanatory writing, as the name implies, has a specific purpose: It is meant to help readers understand something new. The news media engage in explanatory writing every day as they try to help their audiences make sense of what's going on in the world. And many of the textbooks you have read in high school and will read in college use explanatory writing to help you learn.

ASSIGNMENT

Using the reading you've done and your class discussions as background, select a green technology that interests you and conduct research to learn as much as you can about the technology. Then, write an essay in which you explain the technology to an audience unfamiliar with it. As you consider a topic, think broadly about what "green" means. You might, for example, write about a technology used to aid the oil cleanup in the Gulf of Mexico. Or you might explain a set of new smartphone apps that purport to help the environment in some way. Whatever you decide, your goal is to help your readers understand your topic as well as you do after you have conducted your research.

RESEARCH

Your instructor will give you more details about the kind of research you should do as you prepare to write your essay—and may ask you to compile an annotated bibliography of sources as an invention exercise. In general, you should consider sources that can help you:

- Understand and convey to your audience relevant background about your topic. What, for example, do you need to learn and share with your audience in order to prepare them for the explanation to come?

- Contextualize your topic. Where do things stand with the technology now? Has it been the subject of public debate or of legislative action? Are people speaking publicly about your topic? What are they saying?
- Make your readers care about the topic. This is especially important if you think your audience might be hostile, skeptical, or apathetic about the technology you plan to explain. What can you share with your readers to make them want to read what you have to say?
- Explain the technology to your readers. Do you need data, statistics, or other "hard" information to help explain your topic? Do you need expertise from people or sources more knowledgeable about the topic than you? Do you need to include images of some kind? In your paper, you'll need to explain how the technology was developed; what it is used for and who is using it; how it works; and any controversy surrounding it.

A REMINDER

Keep in mind that you're not writing an essay that expresses your opinion or position on the technology (in other words, you are not writing an argument). Your focus should be presenting a clear and accurate explanation of the technology you have chosen.

MAJOR ASSIGNMENT #4: SERVICE LEARNING PROPOSAL AND PROJECT

BACKGROUND

If you're not familiar with them, service learning projects are meant to bring students and their communities closer together to benefit both. These projects—sometimes they encompass entire courses—give students the opportunity to put what they're learning in college to work beyond campus. Ideally, this sharing of knowledge, skills, and concern for the common good works both ways: Students enrich their learning experiences, while the organizations they work with get help they need to better serve the community. Instructors in service learning courses will identify appropriate campus or community organizations and help students develop suitable projects. In an English or writing course, such projects might include proposal, grant, or letter writing; website development; publicity (pamphlets, public service announcements, and the like); or other tasks that put students' communication skills to good use.

COLLABORATION

Students in service learning courses often work in groups, and your instructor may ask you to do the same. This assignment assumes that you'll be working with a small number of classmates, but it can be completed individually, as well.

ASSIGNMENT

This assignment involves several steps, and your group should work closely with your instructor on each one:

- First, identify an environmental organization on campus or in your community that is open to working with service learning students.
- Then, research the organization to learn as much as you can about it—including its history, mission, and methods. You'll probably be able to find some information online or through your library, but you should also consider visiting the organization—or attending a meeting—so you can talk to leaders and other members. (Be certain to consult your instructor before you plan a visit.)

- After you've learned about the organization, identify areas of need that you think fit your group's time and skills. It's important at this point to not take on more than you can handle because once your group commits, the organization will be counting on your help.
- Next, develop a proposal for the work you will do for the organization (see the instructions below).
- Finally, after your instructor approves your proposal and coordinates your project with the organization, get to work!

PROPOSAL

Your proposal should be a clear explanation of the project you would like to undertake for the environmental organization you have chosen. Your instructor will provide more specific details, requirements, and restrictions, based on the course goals as well as the organization and its needs. In general, however, your proposal should include:

- A summary of the organization's mission, membership, and activities, and needs.
- A clear explanation of the project your group would like to undertake.
- A timeline that shows, step by step, how your group will complete the project.
- A brief explanation of how your project will help the organization.

MAJOR ASSIGNMENT #5:
COMPOSING A PERSUASIVE TEXT

BACKGROUND

Persuasive texts come in all shapes, sizes, and technologies—from advertisements and essays; to Facebook pages and YouTube videos; to news shows and websites; to songs, graffiti, and poems. The possibilities are almost limitless. And they all have at least one thing in common: Persuasive texts are designed and composed to get their audiences to think and/or do something specific. This book is filled with persuasive texts—most of them written, but some visual—and you've likely spent time studying some of them to better understand how they work. Now you have the opportunity to try your hand at this important skill.

ASSIGNMENT

Based on the reading you've done in this book, on class discussions, and on your research, compose a persuasive text—written, visual, or multimodal—that addresses an environmental issue or problem. Your goal in this text is to persuade the audience to your way of thinking about your topic and, perhaps, to move them to action. To do these things, you will have to:

- Make your audience care about the topic.
- Find ways to appeal to your audience emotionally and intellectually.
- Be clear about your position and about what, if anything, you want your audience to do.
- Provide ample evidence to persuade the audience that your position is reasonable and worthy of their consideration.
- Address opposing positions.

MODE

Unless your instructor requires a specific kind of text, you will have to decide—based on your topic, purpose, and target audience—the most effective way to convey your message. You might, for example, compose a video public service announcement to post online or to broadcast on your college's cable TV network.

Or you might write an editorial or opinion column for a local newspaper; or you might create a website that incorporates written texts, still images, video, and audio.

RESEARCH

Your instructor will give you more details about the kind of research you should do to for this project—and may ask you to compile an annotated bibliography of sources as an invention exercise. In general, you should consider sources that can help you:

- Convince your audience that they should care about your topic and what you have to say.
- Contextualize your topic.
- Appeal to your audience's intellectual demands by providing data, statistics, or other "hard" evidence to support your position.
- Identify and address positions that oppose your own.

FILMOGRAPHY

FEATURE FILMS

FUTURE SHOCK

Look what we've done! These films use the future—sometimes they're set on Earth, sometimes elsewhere—to try to get us to do something about our treatment of the environment now.

Avatar
Soylent Green
Star Trek IV—The Voyage Home
WALL-E

CORPORATE BAD GUYS VS. ENVIRONMENT

"How many oil spills can we endure?" Steven Seagal—yes, Steven Seagal—asks in *On Deadly Ground*. Like this film, these pit ordinary folks against Big Energy and/or other corporations in battles that often play out in courtrooms and boardrooms.

The China Syndrome
A Civil Action
Erin Brockovich
Fire Down Below
Michael Clayton
On Deadly Ground
Silkwood
Sunshine State

NATURE FIGHTS BACK

Fed up after centuries of mistreatment, the planet—either directly or through one of its larger and angrier inhabitants—decides it's time to take action.

The Day After Tomorrow
Godzilla
King Kong

HUMAN INTERVENTIONS

Recognizing the damage we've inflicted on the planet, the protagonists in these films try to makes things right by intervening on behalf of one small part of the natural world.

Fly Away Home
Free Willy
Hoot
Gorillas in the Mist: The Story of Dian Fossey

DOCUMENTARIES

THE (SORRY) STATE OF THE PLANET

Everything's Cool: A Toxic Comedy About Global Warming
Global Warming: The Signs and the Science
Hotspots
An Inconvenient Truth
Koyaanisqatsi
Manufactured Landscapes
The Yes Men Fix the World

NATURAL (AND UNNATURAL) LIFE AND DEATH

Blue Planet: Seas of Life
The Cove
The End of the Line
Life
Planet Earth
March of the Penguins
Sharkwater
Winged Migration
Yellowstone: Battle for Life

WATER

Blue Gold: World Water Wars
Cadillac Desert
Flow
Frontline: Poisoned Waters

DEVELOPMENT, POLLUTION, AND OTHER DEGRADATIONS

Addicted to Plastic
Blue Vinyl
Dirt! The Movie
The Unforeseen

OIL AND OIL ADDICTION

A Crude Awakening: The Oil Crash
The End of Suburbia: Oil Depletion and the Collapse of the American Dream
Fuel
Who Killed the Electric Car?

INTERVENTIONS AND OTHER ACTIONS

The 11th Hour
American Experience: Earth Days
The Greening of Southie
Ken Burns: The National Parks: America's Best Idea
No Impact Man: The Documentary
Owning the Weather

WORKS CITED

Beavan, Colin. "Life after the Year without Toilet Paper," *No Impact Man*. New York: Farrar, Straus and Giroux, 2009. 211-226. Print.

Brand, Stewart. "Reframing the Problems." *Clock of the Long Now: Time and Responsibility*. New York: Basic Books, 2000. 131-136. Print.

Bullis, Kevin. "The Geoengineering Gambit." *Technology Review*. Massachusetts: MIT Technology Review Press. (January/February 2010). Print.

Carson, Rachel. "The Obligation to Endure." *Silent Spring*. New York: First Mariner Books, 1962. 5-14. Print.

Cliff, Michelle. "Obsolete Geography." *Land of Look Behind*. Ann Arbor, Michigan: Firebrand Books, 1985. Print.

Drash, Wayne. "Brown Pelican Long a Symbol of Survival." *CNN*.com. 15 June 2010. Web.

Eco-America. "Climate and Energy Truths: Our Common Future." Ecoamerica.net. April 2009. 15 June 2010. Web.

Gaye, Marvin. "Mercy Mercy Me (the Ecology)." *Motown Records*. 14 January 2003. LP/digital recording.

Guthrie, Woody. "This Land is Your Land." *Woody Guthrie Publications, Inc*. Los Angeles: Bug Music, 1940. LP/digital recording.

Hayes, Shannon. "Meet the Radical Homemakers." *Yes!*. February, 2010. Web.

Jensen, Derrick and McMillan, Stephanie. *As the World Burns: 50 Simple Things You Can Do to Stay in Denial.* New York: Seven Stories Press. 2007. 1-10. Print.

Jordan, Chris. "Denali/Denial." *Running the Numbers: An American Self-Portrait.* 2006.

Klein, Naomi. "A Hole in the World." *The Guardian.* 19 June, 2010. Print.

Martin, Courtney. "The Population Debate Gets Personal." *The American Prospect.* May, 2010. Web.

Matheson, Christie. *Green Chic: Saving the Earth in Style.* Naperville, Ill.: Sourcebooks, Inc. 2008. 115-130. Print.

Montenegro, Maywa. "A Manifesto for the Planet: an Interview with Stewart Brand." *Seed Magazine.* 3 September, 2009. Web.

Muir, John. "The American Forests [1969]." *The Atlantic Monthly Group.* theatlantic.com. 2010. Web.

Ray, Janisse. *Ecology of a Cracker Childhood.* Minneapolis, Minnesota: Milkweed Editions. 1999. 5-12 and 123-127. Print.

Tidwell, Mike. "To Really Save the Planet, Stop Going Green." *Washington Post.* 6 December 2009. Web.

Todd, Anne Marie. "Prime-Time Subversion: The Environmental Rhetoric of *The Simpsons*" *Enviropop: Studies in Environmental Rhetoric and Popular Culture.* Westport, Connecticut: Praeger Publishers, 2002. 63-80. Print.

Watson, Bruce. "Sounding the Alarm." *Biophile Magazine* 18. Web. [http//:biophile.co.za.]

Weisman, Alan. "Earth Without People." *Discover Magazine.* February, 2005. Web.

Wilson, Edward O. *For the Love of Life.* New York: Knopf Doubleday Publishing Group. 129-140. 2002. Print.